CALL

Chris Hilton was born in Bedfordshire, England. He has been a factory worker, landscape gardener, graphic designer and a dealer in modern first editions. He likes to travel.

CALIENTE

Chris Hilton

Dunbar & Meredith

Distributed by Gardners Books, 1 Whittle Drive, Eastbourne,
East Sussex, BN23 6QH
Tel: +44(0)1323 521555 | Fax: +44(0)1323 521666

British Library Cataloguing in Publication Data
A catalogue record for this book is available from the British
Library.

ISBN   978-0-9569827-0-4

Typeset by Amolibros, Milverton, Somerset
This book production has been managed by Amolibros
www.amolibros.com
Printed and bound by T J International Ltd, Padstow,
Cornwall, UK

"I thought it a fantastic tale. Acerbically and sometimes brutishly written, but full of pace and, most of all, steeped in the sense of the place. Hilton really knows Havana – and there is no substitute for that." *Matthew Parris*

"I must say I was gripped. It has the sweet-and-bitter tang of reality and in my view it will find an eager readership." *John Carey, Merton Professor of English Literature at the University of Oxford*

"Hilton's Cuban adventure is like Havana's mojito cocktail, deceptively smooth and tasty, but underneath is a wicked bite. Take a long draught. Arrange for a friend to take you home." *John Harrison, winner of the 2011 Wales Book of the Year with* Cloud Road

"Almost everyone falls in love with Cuba, intoxicated by its climate, its scenery, its buildings, its music and its people. Some people, like Chris Hilton, are lucky enough to fall in love with a specific Cuban. Not so difficult of course, but it is much harder to write truthfully both about Cuba and about his relationship. In this, Hilton's book is a triumph. He is a delightful guide to the very special atmosphere of Cuba in the last years of the Castro family, and his book should find many readers." *Richard Gott, author of* Cuba: A New History

THANKS TO

Adrianne, Aleena, Celia, Fidel, Grahame, Isabel, Jane, Jessica, Jorgé, José, Lidia, Liz, Mandeep, Marilyn, Mathilde, Mum, Nicole, Noberto, Paul A, Paul S, Raul, Rob, Stefania, Tony, Victoria C, Victoria O, Yuray, Yuriselys

and

Yamilia.

Don't trust a brilliant idea unless it survives a hangover.
Jimmy Breslin

ESCAPE TUNNEL

MARCH – NOVEMBER 2000

I had no real idea how I would get there. I just knew I would go somehow. A review of my finances told me that leaving for *anywhere* was a good idea. I owned a small terraced house that could be sold, but nothing of real value among my possessions. I spent more than I earned every week. I had borrowed heavily and run up several credit cards to their limit. The plan was to get as much money as possible, by whatever means open to me. And go. Perhaps some financial advice would help? I placed an ad in *Private Eye*.

*The above ad appeared in issue 997 of Private Eye on
March 10th 2000*

A reply arrived one week later. It was from an inmate of
an open prison who was serving two years for fraud. He
invited me to visit him. Over the next few months I visited
every weekend. Paul was allowed out on weekend passes.
We drove to a nearby pub and made our plans, or more
accurately, I followed his instructions.

November 24th 2000

I shut down my computer and tidied my desk. People
shuffled, grabbing coats and chatting – a Friday night buzz.
A few people called out – have a great time, don't do anything I wouldn't do. The usual stuff. I had booked two
weeks' holiday and left the next day. I looked over at Jo;
she was watching me. We'd been close, designing logos
together for six years; she helped me through some tough
times. She knew something was going on and she was

pissed off because I hadn't told her. I understood, but I hadn't told anybody. It wasn't personal.

'See you Jo,' I said.

She smiled, a not altogether friendly expression.

'See you Chris, have fun.'

The clock ticked on and we piled towards the door and out into the damp, cold evening. A few more have funs echoed around the car park, mingled with slamming car doors and revved engines. I watched Jo as she pulled out of her space and I waved. She waved back and drove away. I thought I saw her shaking her head. I sat in the empty car park and smoked a cigarette. Then I drove contentedly, dreamily, through the grey, bad-tempered Friday night crawl. I left my car in the Pink Elephant long-stay car park and booked into the Gatwick Hilton. I spent the next three hours roaming the airport, drawing dollars and sterling from various ATMs and exchanges. The next morning I did the same and posted my Pink Elephant ticket to Paul. The car belonged to him now. At four that afternoon I boarded a Cubana flight, direct to Havana. Paul, now free and tagged, called as I sat on the runway,

'All set, Reggie?'

'All set.'

I had $100 000 in an attaché case and considerably more than that in a Channel Island bank account, accessible in Cuba. I didn't set foot in England again for two years.

No one is ever old enough to know better.
Holbrook Jackson

ANYTHING IS POSSIBLE IN CUBA

CHRISTMAS/NEW YEAR 1998/99

Sara and Keith were teachers from England. I didn't want to intrude, but Keith turned out to be a late night drinker and we often sat drinking mojitos into the early hours, became holiday friends and Sara seemed glad of my company during the day. They were fun, if a little naive, and we had some good times together.

One morning at breakfast they said they had a Cuban friend, a young man, a physical education teacher, who was going to show them round a local junior school. Did I want to come along? I did. He turned up after breakfast. He was black, very handsome, shortish, but with a powerful build, cool and polite. He was very well dressed. I sensed a dark humour in his eyes.

'This is José,' said Keith.

He seemed proud of him, an acquisition, a trophy. We walked up Obispo, the long narrow street beside our hotel in Old Havana, and turned into a pretty, tree-lined square, then into a meandering house that turned out to be a school. It was full of happy, noisy children in the maroon uniforms that denoted their age group. José spoke to a teacher who responded with a look of annoyance before nodding and giving him some curt instructions. José then led a class of twenty or so children, crocodile fashion, up to the park opposite the Inglaterra Hotel in central Havana. We sat on a bench and watched José coach the children through a strange set of exercises, which they appeared to thoroughly enjoy. They ran a few small races, all of them cooperating willingly with whatever games he devised. Keith and Sara cooed and aahed, admired the behaviour of the children and commented on how happy they all were. After about thirty minutes José called time and we all walked back to the school, where Keith declared it was time for lunch. José had another brief exchange with the teacher and off we went to a restaurant on O'Reilly, where the food was cheap and we could drink mojitos on the balcony.

Lunch lasted a few hours. The meal was José's reward for the tour. Keith and Sara bombarded him with questions about Cuba. His English was good. I asked him about a situation I'd found myself in a few nights before. A German woman who lived in Cuba had invited me to a poetry reading. After a meandering taxi ride we ended up at a large villa with a lively party in progress and not a poet in sight. The patio held three large metal baths filled with cans of beer submerged in cold water. Bottles of rum lined the perimeter. A band played salsa and everybody there seemed to be doing just as they pleased, which was everything. A long line of expensive cars lined the street;

occasionally one would move as a series of apparently prosperous drunks went out for more alcohol. The German woman, who was enormous, got red-faced and bad temperedly jealous when I danced with any of the women. She was far too much woman for me, so at about 3.00 a.m. I suggested we leave. It was impossible to find a taxi. She proceeded to have a panic attack, convinced she was going to be raped and murdered. I thought that unlikely, but flagged down a passing car and paid the driver to take us back to Old Havana.

'How,' I said to José, 'could this be?'

After all, this was a socialist country, the last bastion of equality and justice. Who owned the villa? Who owned all those cars? Who were all those people? He'd been smiling and laughing throughout my story, trying only slightly to hide his amusement from Keith and Sara. His eyes showed more than just humour when he replied,

'Anything is possible in Cuba.'

Keith and Sara retired for a siesta. I wanted to be alone for a while, a vague feeling of excitement giving me a warm feeling. I recognised it; it had been absent for a few years. I asked José if he would like to go for drink that night, knowing the answer. We arranged to meet at the Sevilla hotel; I didn't want to run into Keith and Sara. We didn't stay at the Sevilla. José took me to a peso restaurant where we ate and drank at Cuban prices. He asked me a lot of questions about my life.

'What about you?' I said.

'What about me?'

I took a sip of my rum; he'd introduced me to Silver

Dry, pure and white; he said that the sugar in mojitos gave bad hangovers. Silver Dry was organic Cuban rum. Eat occasionally and drink water with it, don't overdo it, no hangover. It was clean.

'Well,' I said, 'you're not a teacher for a start.'

He spluttered his drink.

'I'm not?' he said, 'so what am I?'

'You're a hustler,' I said. 'You just borrow those kids. And what were those games you were putting them through?'

He could barely speak for laughing, but he didn't admit anything. I liked that.

'So you had a taste of Cuba,' he said, referring to the party, 'did you like it?'

'Yes, I did.'

'Do you want a woman? I can find you one.'

'No.'

'Why?'

'I don't know. I just don't.'

I got back to the hotel at about 2.00 a.m. No sign of Keith to share a nightcap or two. I ordered a large Silver Dry. Used to company that day, alone I became melancholy. The barman was the inscrutable rather than talkative type, so I sat alone and reviewed my day. The Ambos Mundos was recommended to me by a travel agent, Hemingway had stayed here when he wrote *For Whom The Bell Tolls* – the twenty-four hour bar, the airy high-ceilinged lobby, the monochrome photographs of Hemingway, Fidel, Ché, assorted gangsters, it oozed character – romantic, corrupt and promising.

I nodded to Jorgé, who was on security duties. I'd come in the previous night to find him minding the hotel alone, the other staff were probably sleeping. He came behind the bar to serve me, stood soldierly erect and, I thought disapproving, as I drank and tried to engage him in conversation. I succeeded by buying him drinks. He was a true believer in Fidel and the revolution and by seven the next morning he'd drunk at least eight Cuba Libres, rum and coke. Between us we solved most of the world's troubles. When the day staff arrived he was stumbling around talking happy nonsense. They gave him a few funny looks but said nothing. I thought I may have got him sacked, was pleased to see him still here.

I hardly got started on my drink when something bright and shiny began to seriously affect my peripheral vision. In the bar mirror I saw a Cuban girl had seated herself next to me; she was smiling determinedly at my right profile. She wore a bright red t-shirt; enormous gold earrings swayed and sparkled. I turned to her; she'd gone for the red-hot poker look – red jeans to match. I wasn't in the mood, said 'No gracias' and turned back to the mirror. My reflection didn't improve my mood. She wasn't in the least discouraged and asked in precise, beautifully spoken English, if she could have a beer. I bought her a beer.

I continued to ignore her while the barman studiously ignored both of us and she smiled unconcernedly. Jorgé chatted to his security colleague by the door. I couldn't figure out how she had got into the bar. During my stay I'd seen a few men, not the best advertisements for the Caucasian male, attempting to take Cuban girls to their rooms. They were politely but firmly stopped at the lift by hotel security, and told that it was against the law. Single Cuban girls were generally not allowed into hotels at all without good reason. Prostitution is illegal in Cuba. That, of course, is irrelevant. I'd seen Cuban girls with tourists, I'd been approached by girls of varied age and beauty, and declined, not through any moral superiority or lack of desire – I just couldn't see how it all worked, didn't feel comfortable with it. More importantly, I hadn't been impressed with many of the men I'd seen parading with stunningly beautiful Cuban girls on their arm. I didn't want to look like them.

But here she was. Jorgé and his friend had found something fascinating to watch through the window, were discussing it at length. The barman busied himself being inscrutable. I wondered if I'd overdone the rum, because if anyone but me could see the lady in red, still drinking beer and smiling, they showed no sign of it. But, it was two in the morning, respectable residents were tucked up in bed; things change after midnight no matter where you are in the world. She'd been allowed in. She knew somebody. Interesting. Fed up with my reflection I turned towards her. The smile remained in place, an impish child-like smile that seemed to say, 'OK, what shall we do next?', as though we'd been together all day. Her hair was cut short above her ears, curly, but she'd sort of straightened the top two inches and gelled it upwards. It could have looked masculine, but Cuban women don't do masculine, and I was suddenly aware that she was quite beautiful. Her brown eyes flashed at me in the light. How do they do that? Mid-to-late twenties, light brown skin with high cheekbones, tapered chin, carefree smile framing perfect white teeth.

If I'd wanted her I'd have felt intimidated. I was in my late forties then and though I thought I was in good shape, my reflection disagreed. I was pale and tired. But I was only buying her a beer, wasn't I? The day's drinking had jaded my appetite for anything other than sleep. I'd buy her another beer, have one more rum and go to bed. Yes. I ordered, same again. The barman somehow managed to serve us without acknowledging our presence.

'Take the drinks here,' she said, 'is more comfortable.'

She indicated a dozen small tables away from the bar, next to the windows and the street. I said no, that I would drink up and go to bed.

'Me too,' she said.

'No.' I pointed above me; my room was on the fifth floor, 'I go here, you go there.' I indicated the door. She smiled as though I was being very silly, picked up the drinks and took them to a table. I followed.

Her name was Irene. She asked me where I was from, what did I do? Did I have any family? Was I alone? Why? Her English was good, though she said she spoke only 'a little'. Where did she learn? At school. Did she live in Havana? No, she was from Santiago, but she had family here. She had a young daughter in Santiago. She was bright and easy to talk to. My drink was finished and I wanted another. She changed to rum and ordered some snack biscuits.

'Are you hungry?'

She nodded. I gave her five dollars. There are twenty-four-hour bars along the length of Obispo. She took the money and rose to go.

'You stay here,' she said.

'OK. After this,' I raised my drink, 'I sleep.'

'Me too'.

Ten minutes later she was back. She had some chicken and what appeared to be hot crisps. She offered me some. No thanks. She offered the change. I shook my head.

'When you finish I go up, you go out,' I said.

'No. I stay with you.'

'It's impossible.'

'Is possible. Give the man ten dollars, no problem.'

So that's how it worked. I looked over at Jorgé. He and his friend had been watching, now they looked quickly away. Jorgé talked very loudly, indicating how dark it was tonight, or how large the moon, or something equally important.

I thought about it. I wanted to want to, but I really didn't want to, not now. She had no intention of going anywhere. Every time I said that I was going upstairs she replied, 'Me too,' and shrugged, as though it was inevitable. I wondered if she just needed a room for the night, what was left of it, though she didn't seem concerned. She didn't seem concerned about anything. In fact, if she could get any looser, the rum was making her so; she was enjoying herself. I tried another approach, took twenty dollars from my pocket, put the note on the table. She stared at it evenly.

'Take this. Now I go this way, you go that way. Do you understand?'

'Yes, I understand. Is a present for me.'

'Yes, a present. Now you have to go.'

'No. I stay with you.'

She sipped her drink, shrugged and smiled. I gave in.

Apart from anything else I needed to sleep.

'You go to your room,' she said, 'five minutes.'

I walked to the lift. Jorgé dragged himself away from his conversation and followed me, opened the concertina doors. I handed him ten dollars.

'Do you know her?' I said.

'Irene. Yes. I know her family. A good family.'

He was soldierly again. His moustache was intimidating. Had he set this up? Enjoyed our conversation from the night before? Or just noticed the cash? True communist he was, but everyone needed an angle to stay above the peso economy.

'I've never seen her before.'

'She likes you.'

'She doesn't know me.'

'She likes you.' He shrugged.

In my room I cleared stuff off the other single bed. I didn't feel any different about wanting to sleep, but was curious about what she'd want, what she'd do. A knock at the door. Jorgé had brought Irene. She walked past me into the room and looked around. I was about to speak when she came towards me with a look, half predatory, half amused and kissed me full on the lips for a long time. Her kiss woke me like an electric shock and, suddenly, I was wide-awake, tingling, alive and ready for more. She broke off, studied my face and smiled.

'Wait here,' she said, and disappeared into the shower.

I waited.

I flew home two days later. José came with me to the airport. We sat at a bar waiting.

12

'Will you come back?

'Yes.' I surprised myself by how sure I was. 'But it won't be until this time next year, Christmas. I hate Christmas in England. I have to make some money. I'll stay for a few weeks next time.'

We exchanged addresses and numbers. I hated goodbyes and I didn't want to go home. I never did.

'You are leaving Cuba without having a Cuban woman.'

'No.'

He gave me his full attention.

'When?'

'She stayed in my hotel room for the last three nights.'

'Did you like her?'

'Yes, she was good fun.'

'Fun?'

I explained. He shook his head and laughed.

'How much did you pay her?'

'I didn't pay her. We went out and I paid. I gave her a present last night.'

'That means she likes you. Was she beautiful?'

'Yes, in a funny way.'

'Was she good?'

'None of your business.'

'So she was good,' he said. 'All Cuban women are good. That's why men come here and fall in love. The women are uninhibited, not like in Europe. Men come here, women too, and then they keep coming back. Everybody loves Havana.'

'I'm not in love,' I said.

'Are you sure?'

'I'm sure.'

'When you come back you will fall in love.'
'I don't think so.'
'We will see,' he said.

When you go in search of honey you must expect to be stung by bees.
Joseph Joubert

YAMILIA

HAVANA, CHRISTMAS/NEW YEAR 1999/2000

I got to my room at the Ambos Mundos at ten p.m. Cuban time – three a.m. my time. Due to meet José the next day, tonight I wanted to prowl alone. Two large white rums revived me and I wandered up Obispo, which was then still sparsely lit: quiet, dark stretches were interspersed with bursts of brightness, music and laughter from the bars. Shadowy figures moved in side streets and doorways.

Obispo was changing. Building materials littered parts of the narrow street, which was being made fit for tourists. The crumbling, tall, colonial buildings were being slowly, very slowly, restored to their original construction. Bulbous, long-necked bottles containing a rainbow of coloured perfumes lined the top shelves of a pharmacy that had been rubble a year before. Behind a long hardwood counter were rows of herbal medicines, hand-labelled with their names and medicinal properties. I remembered watching the Cuban workers the previous year, appearing to be doing little or nothing in a mess of dust and debris, occasionally hand-sawing a plank of wood. Yet they had been craftsmen, working at their own pace. There would be no real profit in it, the bottom line wouldn't make sense – this was craftsmanship for its own sake – beautiful, unique and idiosyncratic. Cuban.

An echoing tap of heels on concrete interrupted my thoughts. A shimmering, long white dress emerged from the gloom, clacking hurriedly, noisily toward me. She moved, not at all gracefully, into the pool of light where I stood. I lit a cigarette and watched as she passed. Long black hair swept back, something red holding it in place, the low cut dress revealing a glint of gold against light brown skin. She gave me a glance of severe disinterest as she passed, unsmiling, head proudly back. She seemed angry. The dress flowed loosely around her legs but clung tightly to her prominent Latin bottom, defying gravity as it swayed hypnotically away from me into another patch of gloom. I threw my cigarette into the street and walked behind her. She didn't look back, appeared to be having trouble with her heels, looking down and, I thought, cursing them as she walked. She was still moving fast though, and getting further away from me. Near the end of Obispo she stopped in response to a shout from some boys on a street corner. As I got closer I heard her laughing and joking with them. She gave me the briefest of glances.

As I approached she set off again. I closed the distance and walked beside her; even in heels she was small. She stared straight ahead, ignoring me. Only when I spoke did she acknowledge my presence,

'Buenos noches.'

She looked up at me but didn't stop or speak.

'Do you speak English?' I said.

'You are English?'

'Si.'

'¿Hablar Espanol?' she said.

'Muy poco.' Very little.

'I no speak English.'

'You just did.' She laughed and the harshness left her face, utterly changing her. She stared at me as we walked, a direct, challenging and confident stare that said 'Well, what are you going to do now?'

'Would you like to come for a drink with me?' I said.

'Like? What is like?'

'Happy. Feliz.'

'Happy,' she repeated the word, was silent for a few long seconds as she clacked and tottered on her heels, 'OK, me happy.'

'You said you couldn't speak English.'

'I don't.'

We reached the end of Obispo, emerged into the weak light of the Plaza de Armas, silent apart from the chatter of tourists at a pavement restaurant. Much of the square was bathed in shadow. Replica gas street lamps gave a pleasant, low, seductive glow; opposite us the Santa Isabel, rumoured to be the height of luxury and the haunt of Hollywood actors, bathed in their yellow light – three stories and twenty-seven rooms of expensive exclusivity. Bats darted between the darkened museum, the castle and the tall ceiba trees lining the square. It could have been a quiet provincial scene, but listen carefully and there was music, just a few minutes walk away.

'Where shall we go?' I said.

'Where you want?'

'I don't know. Do you live in Havana?'

'Si.'

'So take me somewhere.'

We walked to a very public tourist bar by the seafront. Crowded tables spread outside and over a wide pavement. It appeared to be full and we joined the queue waiting to be placed. She shouted at a waiter who smiled and greeted her; they embraced and kissed cheeks. He found us a table close to the usual smiling, energetic musicians. The female singer waved to her as we sat down. I ordered rum and she had a beer. Suddenly feeling very tired, I explained that I'd been travelling for sixteen hours.

'Where you from?'

'London.'

'What your work?'

'Computers.'

She lowered her head and smiled. When she raised it again she checked out my jacket, hung on the chair. Her eyes moved over my shirt, watch, shoes and lastly, my face. She spent a long time there. Some women can check you out and appraise your worth in a millisecond. This woman was as subtle as a sledgehammer. I held her gaze, wondered if she was mulata: half Spanish, half African. Her skin was a light, tawny brown but appeared to change with the light; her large, almond shaped eyes dark, almost black as she assessed me without embarrassment. Although she was very young, early twenties I thought, her eyes and manner spoke of experience way beyond her years. I couldn't place her: Latin, African – Indian? Was there still Indian blood in Cuba? I thought the Spanish had wiped them out, but I wasn't sure.

'How old you are?' she said.

'Forty-eight.'

She thought about it. Her thought processes showed on her face like subtitles.

'How old me?'

I thought: twenty-three.

'Twenty,' I said.

Her face lit up with pleasure.

'Veinte cinco.' Twenty-five, she said.

I didn't know about dollar shops then. How some lived above, or way above the peso economy. I just thought this was a poor country trying its best in the face of spiteful sanctions. I looked over her clothes. Cuban people of all ages manage to look good no matter what they wear; they put something with style together. This woman had style but it hadn't come cheap: gold around her neck and wrist, a nice watch, the new looking silk dress – I wondered where it had come from.

'Where did you get such nice clothes?'

'You think we don't have good clothes in Cuba? You think because you come from rich country we have nothing? I buy from Hemingway Marina, from Habana Libre. You come here and you think we are shit.'

'No. I don't think you are shit. Lo siento. I'm sorry. I

don't know Cuba. Your clothes are very stylish. I didn't know you could buy them here.'

Her face darkened, her lips compressed and white with anger. She wouldn't look at me. She stubbed out her cigarette, almost destroying the ashtray. Her eyelids flickered. She sat back in her chair and looked around for a distraction, found it in one of the waiters and shouted out a greeting, smiling as the storm clouds disappeared. She turned back to me, all as before.

'What is your name?'

'Chris. ¿Como te llamas?'

'Yamilia.'

'What is your work?'

'Enfermera.' A nurse. Had she always been a nurse? No. Before that she had been a gymnast, she had represented Cuba at the Los Angeles' Olympics.

'You've been to America?'

'No America. This is America. Estados Unidos. Si. And I live in France for two years.'

'Where in France?'

'In Monte Carlo, and Genoa in Italia. I see the cars in Monaco and the pelicula in Cannes.'

'¿Pelicula?'

'Si. Movies.'

'The Cannes Film Festival?'

'Si.'

'Why were you in France?'

'A medico, a doctor. He come to Cuba and take me to France.'

'And you came back.'

'Si. Estupido, much money, very stupid.'

'So you came home.'

'Si.'

If he'd sent her home or if she'd come by choice I didn't ask. At around two the bar began closing. Yamilia hadn't made any suggestions, looked happy and relaxed. I was very tired and probably didn't *need* a woman, but I wanted her. I wanted to ask her to my room, but thought that would have the feel of a one-night stand, a transaction – what if I wanted to see her again? I looked up. She was watching me with a two-thousand-year-old stare, wise and knowing.

'Me no prostituta,' she said.

'I don't care. No importante.'

I met her eyes. Sometimes they would slide away as she talked. Not now. She held my stare and smiled. I decided to resolve any conflict in the morning, or afternoon, or whenever I woke up. If I woke up.

'Come to my hotel for a drink.'

'A drink?'

'Si.'

She pondered what a drink might mean.

'OK.'

At the hotel it took five minutes for the bar staff to appear and serve us. It was a twenty-four hour bar, but there were no customers.

'They sleep,' she said. 'They no like. They no happy.'

'Happy.' She repeated the word, shook her head and laughed. Then she shouted an order at the barman who jumped and served us with two large rums. After the first beer she'd matched me, rum for rum, all night. Apart from relaxing her slightly I saw no signs that she'd been drinking at all. We sat away from the bar by a large open window looking out onto Obispo. She shivered.

'Frio.'

'You are cold?'

It was late December, nearly Christmas. The temperature was around seventy degrees.

'Take my jacket.'

She put on the jacket; charcoal with pin stripes, released her hair, fluffed it around her ears and shoulders. It spread behind her, thick, shiny and slightly curled. She shook it and pushed it back from her face, buttoned the jacket and hugged herself. I couldn't take my eyes away from her. She warmed herself inside the jacket, disconcerted by my stare. She had no idea of the effect she was having, and the fact that she was unconscious of it made her even more attractive. She picked up her glass and clinked it against mine.

'Salut,' she said.

She laughed and pointed to the window.

'That man. Mira. Look.'

I turned and looked out at the street. A man stood there, his arms held out, palms up in supplication. He was around thirty, maybe Scandinavian, a tourist. He shrugged his shoulders and raised his eyebrows at me. He blew a kiss at Yamilia and walked off. She laughed again.

'I think he like me. Comico.'

So that's who she'd been rushing to meet in her high heels; her date.

'Si, comico,' I said.

As she relaxed her voice took on a seductive deep tone, personal, attentive and interested. Her laugh was sexy and musical – whenever she smiled or laughed I wanted to make her do it again because it made me feel good. I asked her to come to my room.

'Is impossible.'

'It's possible.'

In the room she walked straight to the balcony and watched the street below.

'Hemingway write famous book here,' she said.

'Here?' I said, joking, meaning this room.

She stared at me as though I was insane.

'No. Not here, upstairs. In room for tourists.'

She had a toned gymnast's body, not the slight East European version, but one with all the Latin curves in miniature. She was almost entirely physically passive at first, but I sensed her gauging my desire. She was alert, interested and calculating. When I climaxed, loudly, she propped herself on her elbows and watched. Rather than sleepy I felt energised. As she dressed I put on a pair of baggy shorts, picked up my wallet and flicked through it.

'You want give me money?'

'You want me to?'

'I have money,' she said, as if the subject of money was so vulgar she wouldn't lower herself to discuss it. She finished dressing and sat on the other bed. I told her I'd been learning Spanish and quoted silly phrases at her:

'We put on the TV after dinner.'

'They go to school by bus.'

'I washed my hair today.'

She sat, chin on hands, and watched me. I was high now. I launched into a monologue, part English and part awful Spanish about Fidel and Cuba and the United States. She sat and looked and listened.

'What you say?' she said.

Then she undressed again, pulled my shorts off and made love to me. She smiled the whole time. Warmer, perhaps more herself now, but still holding something back. Somehow I doubted she was a nurse. I was left in no doubt at all that she'd been a gymnast.

She dressed quickly. It was 5.00a.m.

'When you wake up, call me.'

She wrote down her number and left.

I got up three hours later and ate breakfast on the roof of the hotel. A gorgeous day, like a late, warm English summer. The quality of the light alone revived me. Later in the lobby I listened to an enormous Cuban, whose backside spilled over the piano stool, play lovely music. He said Hello. Everybody at the hotel remembered me from the year before. José turned up at midday. I told him about Yamilia. I said I was going hire a car and see the country; that I would ask Yamilia to come with me. The disappointment showed on his face but he said:

'It will be good for you to see Cuba, see how the people live.'

I phoned and arranged to meet her in the lobby the next day. After breakfast I went for a walk and hired a high-range Audi, realising uncomfortably that I wanted to impress her. I browsed the book stalls in the Plaza Armas as I waited for the allotted time. Returning to the hotel I scanned the lobby. She wasn't there so I sat at the bar to wait. The barman mixed my mojito and studied me curiously,

'Your woman is here,' he said, 'she waits for twenty minutes.'

I turned and checked the lobby again. It was almost empty. In the far corner a young girl in jeans and t-shirt sat alone on a white sofa, a soft drink on the low table in front of her. I watched the barman as he mixed lime, sugar and mint leaves into the white rum and soda. I paid and raised my eyebrows in query. He nodded at the girl. I looked again. She sat primly with her hands in her lap, unsmiling, staring straight at me. Yamilia? I felt confused and embarrassed. Finally she smiled and I went to her table.

'You don't know me,' she said.

That was true. She looked sixteen. She was different, Asian today, perhaps Balinese, a tiny, golden Asian; hair bunched behind her head, pulled tight to her scalp. She wore old jeans, trainers and a brightly coloured striped t-shirt. She smiled primly, beautifully; I found it hard to speak. Only her eyes and the sensuous turn of her mouth told me who she was. She wore no makeup and with her hair back her face looked thinner, smaller – still supremely confident though, enjoying my confusion.

'You look different. I didn't recognise you.'

'You like?' She said, with a coyness that didn't suit her.

I shrugged.

'You're OK.'

She kicked me.

'I hired a car.'

'Si?'

'I want to see the country. Do you want to come with me?'

'Where you go?'
'I don't know.'
'Can we go see my mama?'
'Where is your mama?'
'Camaguey. One day to drive.'
'OK.'

The drive was my first real experience of life outside Havana. The three-lane freeway was mostly deserted and the kilometres sped by comfortably, no need for too much concentration. I was free to take in the mainly flat farming land, interspersed with green rolling hills, land producing tobacco, sugar, coffee and assorted exotic fruit and vegetables. Towering royal palms swayed, fragile looking but indestructible, above thatched farmers' cottages. The sky appeared vast, an endless horizon, incongruous for a small island (Cuba is slightly smaller than Great Britain), like the Big Sky in parts of the USA, eighty miles to the north.

We settled into an easy companionship of music, conversation and comfortable silence. I watched her occasionally, still fascinated by her changeability. She was still the young girl I'd met yesterday, having swapped her jeans for shorts. She was lithe and tomboyish, often clambering over the seats to retrieve something from our luggage or to sleep for a while. She seemed able to sleep at will and then be wide awake again. We spoke English and she asked me to explain any words she didn't understand. I'd put a word into context for her, give the Spanish equivalent if I could and it quickly became part of her vocabulary. She sometimes spoke a mixture of Spanish, French and English, had a certain gift for languages that I lacked completely.

When I stopped for petrol we ate and drank at the roadside cafes and restaurants, depressingly similar in appearance to such places the world over, but most definitely Cuban in terms of service and atmosphere: unhurried, casual, mostly friendly, sometimes indifferent. She seemed happy and I wondered if it was me or that she just enjoyed the change, the moment, the trip to see her mother – would she be like this in any company? She was certainly curious about my life, about life in England, about everything. During a conversation about money she said:

'You come from good country. I come from shit country.'

And I remembered her indignation from two nights before when I'd clumsily implied that good clothes couldn't be found in Cuba. This was something I would encounter throughout my time later in Cuba: A mocking criticism of their country contradicted by a fierce pride in being Cuban and extreme sensitivity to criticism of it.

The drive took about ten hours. Her mother's cottage was in Lugareno, a village thirty miles beyond Camaguey. We stopped at a roadside bar just before arriving, where Yamilia bought masses of beer and rum. I saw why when we arrived. She had obviously phoned ahead and we were greeted by a mass of grinning, laughing, overexcited people of all ages. I was dazed and confused despite introductions and glad to find a rocking chair on the porch, where a glass of rum was thrust into my hand.

Yamilia couldn't stop hugging and touching her mother, pulling away for introductions and then returning to her. Slowly, before the night turned into a blur of fiesta, music and dancing, I managed to figure out who was family and who just happened to turn up. I stayed on the porch and let Yamilia bring people to me as I became more sociable and my Spanish improved with the rum. Her mother and a sister, Sally, lived in the cottage with Fifi, a brother and occasional resident. Her father, whom her mother hadn't spoken to in ten years, was visiting for my benefit. Zenaida, another sister, was also visiting. The rest were friends and neighbours. Yamilia was a late addition to a large family – there were three more brothers elsewhere. She was the baby of the family, the favourite, spoilt by everyone, watched over, particularly by her mother, with a protective, concerned, but tolerant air. Baby or not she had left home at fifteen and survived alone in Havana for ten years. She was probably tougher than any of them.

Her mother was black with a gentle, long-suffering expression; Sally too was black, as was Fifi who was much darker, tall, beautiful and manic. He smiled constantly, seemed to be in a permanent state of excitement.

'Fifi is crazy,' said Yamilia.

Sally, according to Yamilia, was 'simple'; in her mid-thirties she had never left home 'and never fucks nobody'. Luis, her father, was Haitian: tall, slim, handsome, dignified and pale skinned. He sat with me on the porch avoiding his wife. Zenaida was lighter-skinned like Yamilia and just as beautiful, fuller of face, taller and older. She had her six-year-old son with her. Yamilia caught me watching her,

'If you meet Zenaida first, you choose her,' she said.

Later I supported Luis as we wove unsteadily home from a New Year's Eve party at the village hall, where a horse had been invited. In Camaguey I bought a live grain-fed pig, which was trussed up and put in the boot of my car. That night we had a fiesta. I watched them kill and prepare the pig and was eating it an hour later. Firstly they fried the skin: scratchings. A villager said that if I ate them all night I could drink as much rum as I liked without getting a hangover. He was right. I allowed Fifi to drive my car, and as we drove around he would pick up as many hitchhikers as we could fit in. One day we drove back to the village with eleven people in the car, music blaring.

I lived more in those weeks than I'd lived in years. She didn't ask for money. One day she said:

'I'll take you somewhere.'

We arrived at a car park and I looked around. It was a designer store.

'Yamilia,' I said, 'this is a shop.'

'Magnifique, mi amor,' she said, as she walked towards it.

I saw that, like me, she had her manic side.

'A little crazy is good,' she said.

I once asked her if everything was OK. She studied me as though I were a child.

'When is everything OK in this life?' she said.

As we lay on a beach at night in San Pedro I told her that some of the stars she could see were not really there, that they had died and disappeared many years ago. They were so far away and it took the light so long to reach us that we didn't know they were gone yet. She turned to face me from where she lay, pointed at her head and said,

'You have something wrong here.'

At a club in Santiago de Cuba I paid one of the three bouncers on the door and went to the bar for drinks. I looked around for Yamilia. She was talking to them. They towered above her, big, tall black men in suits with shaved heads. She had her hands on her hips, her head tilted to one side, nodding to emphasise a point she was making. She finger-poked the chest of one of them. They looked down at her, impassive and expressionless, the way bouncers do everywhere, until you find yourself picking yourself up from the floor. My drinks arrived and I turned to pay. She was beside me.

'They make you pay too much,' she said, and handed me two dollars.

I looked back at the bouncers. All three were watching her, one was shaking his head.

We were arrested in Santiago for riding two on a bike, a mere excuse to fine a tourist – everybody did it. Further along the coast we lay on black-sanded beaches beneath the mountains of the Sierra Maestra, where Fidel, Che and eighty compañeros launched the first successful revolution in Cuba's violent history. On a clear night from their highest point, we watched the shimmering lights of Haiti and Jamaica.

On the drive back to Havana we stopped at a roadside bar. I noticed she'd taken two hundred dollars from the glove compartment. I asked her to give it back. She widened her eyes and smiled.

'Give it back or you walk home.'

We sat in the car facing each other.

'Me? Walk?'

She reached over to the backseat, picked up my jacket

and got out of the car. She put it on, patted the pockets and smiled through the window. The jacket contained my wallet and passport. She walked towards the restaurant smiling over her shoulder. I waited a few minutes before following, and joined her at a table.

'You see all these places, fiestas, photographs of my life, stay with my family? And you don't like two hundred dollars?'

She had a point, but I sensed danger in giving in. I gave her a hundred and fifty.

Before we reached Havana I stopped on a small bridge by a lake where I wanted to take some pictures. I got out and leaned against the railings with my camera. Below was a man-made outlet with sheer concrete sides, perhaps part of a water supply. Clear shallow water flowed gently under the bridge. She asked if she could use the camera. I said she could and lectured her about being careful, keeping the strap around her wrist so as not to drop it to the water below. She listened patiently and then ran off a few photographs. She handed the camera back and I rested it on the railings for support, intending to use the zoom. And I dropped it. I didn't use the strap and my camera fell into the water twelve feet below.

'Fuck!' I said, embarrassed and angry at the lost camera and, more importantly, the lost photographs.

'I'll get it,' she said.

She walked around the side of the railings, along a grass verge above the concrete sides of the outlet and stood above a thin metal pipe below the top of the wall. She crouched at the edge before slipping over, holding the edge of the wall for a few seconds before dropping into the water below. She walked to where the camera had fallen, picked it out of the water and shook it.

'Is OK,' she said, 'we can dry in the sun.'

I stood above the metal pipe wondering how she was going to get out.

'Catch,' she said, and tossed the camera up to me.

I lay it on the grass and turned to help her. The metal pipe was way above her reach. The wall leaned at a very slight angle, pockmarked with a few bumps and dips. She used them to gain a grip and sprung herself up to the pipe two feet below me. I moved closer to the edge to pull her up. She was swinging by one arm, smiling up at me; her arms were thin and barely muscled, but she seemed quite comfortable supporting her weight:

'Chris, get out of the way,' she said between laughs.

'I'll help you,' I said.

'No, get out of the way.'

I stepped back. She jerked her other hand to the pipe and swung her feet up onto the grass, then pushed on the pipe to move her upper body up too. Only then did she take my hand as I pulled her to her feet.

'You must be careful with your camera, Chris,' she said, and threw back her head and laughed as she walked back to the car, her soaked trainers squelching. 'Come on, we will dry it in the window.'

I stood and watched until she was in the car before I moved. The music had started up again before I got to it.

It was late when we got back to the Ambos Mundos. We ate at the roof top restaurant then went down to the lobby. It was my last night but we were both too tired to go out. Tonight, after three weeks together, we would have to make do with a few hours before reception called and asked her to leave. Jorgé showed her into my room. I was already on the bed and she lay down beside me. The ringing phone woke us as the first dim light of my last day crept on to the balcony. She lay with her arm draped across me; both of us still in our clothes. I watched her sleepily as she gathered her things. She bent and kissed me:

'Phone me later.'

'OK.'

She stopped by the door and turned around, momentarily confused. She looked down at her clothes and at me on the bed.

'Mmm,' she said, 'Chris and Yamilia sleep.'

My flight was at midnight. I checked out of my room at midday and settled down in the bar with José. I was full of myself and the trip. I still believed that it was just Cuba that I'd fallen in love with. That she'd been the catalyst. He listened. He was glad that I'd seen life in Cuba but he didn't say much.

'I think I'm going to come back here to stay,' I said.

'When?'

'Soon.'

'Can you do it?'

'I think so.'

'Where is Yamilia?'

'I have to phone.'

'I know her,' he said.

'So?'

'Be careful.'

I wanted to see her, but some vestige of self-protection,

a desire not to get involved, prevented me from picking up the phone. An hour later she turned up. She glared at me before greeting José; they kissed each other's cheeks.

'You no phone,' she said.

At eleven I was at the airport with Yamilia. In the taxi she said,

'José is your friend?'

'Yes, I think so.'

'He is a Chuchillo, a knife man,' she said.

We had a minor row and I turned my back on her. I walked to the departure gate convinced that I didn't care, but also convinced that she'd follow me, say sorry, kiss and make up before I got there. She didn't.

As the plane sped down the runway I still thought that I didn't care. As soon as we settled on to the flight path I ordered a large rum, chatted to the hostess, picked up the book I'd chosen to read. I couldn't concentrate. I had a pain in my chest that felt like a heart attack. The stewardess asked me if I was OK. Was there anything she could do for me? No, there wasn't anything she could do for me. I looked around the first-class cabin: just a few men playing with their laptops, no women. I went to the toilet and masturbated, came back to my seat thinking that would take care of it. It didn't. I felt dizzy, couldn't collect my thoughts at all. I thought I'd made myself tough and impregnable – no one could reach me. So what was this? The hostess was watching me with calculated concern. I didn't know what to do with myself. I tried to read my book. I couldn't even see the words. I ordered a bottle of rum and drank it as I sped towards England and work and my life. The life I had under so much control.

At Gatwick I phoned Yamilia.

'I'm coming back.'

'You come back?'

'Next week. For two days.'

'You crazy.'

'A little crazy is good,' I said.

I booked a return flight before I left the airport. I would fly out at 4p.m. on Friday, arriving at 10p.m. Cuban time and leave at midnight on Sunday. I called in sick at work on Friday morning: the flu, I thought. That same night she was waiting for me at José Marti Airport. Fifty hours with Yamilia. I was in love. Seriously. Oh dear.

Many people die at 25 and aren't buried until they're 75.
Max Fritsch

ARRIVAL

NOVEMBER 25TH, 2000

The lights of Havana below stirred an excitement in me
bordering on euphoria, a childish feeling, but still level-
headed, tinged with the knowledge that I'd done this
myself. I had a dream, made a plan and here I was. The
city appeared warm and welcoming to me then. This wasn't
just another holiday. This was my home. Home free.

   The taxi took us to Rosa's flat in Villa Pan Americana,
a few miles outside Havana. We'd stayed there before on
other visits. I was in a daze, exhausted, but also wide awake
and buzzing. Yamilia was strange too, maybe not quite
believing that after months of worried phone calls, doubt-
ing not so much my ability to do this, but my desire to
come back to her, I was here. I paid Rosa up front for three
months. I wanted to seal my permanence quickly and show
them I meant this. We went to the only club in town at
the Villa Pan Americana hotel. I floated in and out of
alertness, using dregs of spare adrenalin. Yamilia didn't

suggest a quiet night or sleep. She knew me pretty well; knew that I would have bursts of energy, that I would be tired and then wake up suddenly, so she let the evening go at its own pace, my pace. It would end when we fell into bed.

She laughed as I danced my strange salsa, mixed up with every other dance I'd ever danced and every emotion I was feeling, while the rum did its best to soothe my jangled nerves. I looked into her black eyes, searching for kindness maybe, but not really caring if it was there or not. I danced with the energy of the damned, thinking that such nights were precious, that it could be my last. And that night – and many to come – I felt truly, miraculously alive. The night seemed to welcome me. At night, or more accurately, the early hours, dark, with like souls, there is the capacity for hedonism, maybe just a hint of violence and corruption in the air – not too much, because that makes everyone sad and irredeemable – a fine line, one that's impossible to find and walk most of the time. Tonight I found it and I was happy. I stretched the dancing and the drinking and took energy from the night. I thought about the future and I dared God to stop me. I threw back my head and laughed.

Later I stared into her eyes again and felt as though she was trying to envelop me, swallow me up; she held onto me as though she would drown if she let go, and I, in turn, tried to disappear into her. And then I remember waking to a smile and coffee. I'd slept for fifteen hours.

The next day we took a taxi to Cubacel in Miramar, among the rich and the foreign embassies. At that time only

Cubacel's mobile phones worked in Cuba; you had to buy and rent from them. I called Paul as we took the return journey.

'Where are you?' he said.

'I'm in a taxi on the malecon with Yamilia.'

'The malecon?'

'The sea front in Havana.'

'So you're mobiled. How does it work?'

'I bought the phones. I pay for the phone time. Have to go to Cubacel for top-ups. It's slow.'

'Phones?'

'I bought one for Yamilia too.'

'Is that wise?'

'Local calls only on hers.'

'OK. Is the phone time expensive?'

'I don't know.'

'The seafront in Havana. Beautiful woman by your side. You bastard.'

'I know.'

I prefer young girls. Their stories are shorter.
Thomas Mcguane

VILLA PAN AMERICANA

Villa Pan Americana lacked the noise and chaos of Havana, which was fine. Modern flats, some nice houses, a few rows of shops and the hotel built for the Pan American games in 1991. A one street town with a couple of small supermarkets, some bars and restaurants, dollar clothes shops and the hotel. Havana was a twenty-minute taxi ride; the hotel had a good pool, a decent club and the Playas del Este, Easterly Beaches, were just a few miles away.

I became comfortable shopping and in the bars; knew people to say hello to and practise my Spanish. Rosa came and cooked if we wanted, she stayed with relatives while she rented her flat. She was a young, trim fortyish, white with the usual long black hair and tolerant of rather than friendly towards Yamilia. Yamilia could cook, and occasionally she did, but mostly we ate out. We had a tame policeman. I liked him. He came to the flat with his girlfriend and always brought a couple of beers. After a few weeks he stopped coming. I asked Yamilia,

'They move him another place,' she said, 'Fidel no like them get comfortable.'

Two weeks in I met Raul, a local doctor, and Lucia, his nurse. I went down with a fever, brought on through the change in lifestyle and exhaustion according to Raul – a cleansing process. Yamilia recognised the signs and called Raul immediately. He lived alone in a similar flat. Lucia had a larger place, a family and a surgery below. Raul took an interest in my health and Lucia in our relationship. I got advice on the perils of smoking and rum from one and coaching for my sex life from the other. Sexo was Lucia's favourite subject; she became a regular visitor to the flat. As for Raul, I was to need his help many times over the next eighteen months.

The first few weeks were better than I'd dared hope for. Yamilia accepted my permanence and saw that I had no intention of leaving. The tension and doubt of our previous times together, her doubts that I would ever return for good and the horrible goodbyes at the airport were gone. My body's slow adjustment to the fact that I didn't have any work to get up for, didn't have a mortgage to pay, that I could do anything I wanted in a sunny, exciting country with pleasure-loving people, improved my health and my temper. Sleeping with a beautiful woman every night, a woman whose sexual appetite seemed greater than mine brought an almost Zen-like calm. I felt lighter, younger and full of spare energy. I began to like people again. I realised I'd been carrying a burden of stress on my shoulders for years, everyday stress that many people feel – not sleeping enough, struggling through the same stultifying routine, supplementing it with alcohol, entertainment, day after day after day; too much coffee, too much traffic, too much work, too little money – too little life.

Despite what happened later I will always remember those first few months. I think of it now and my heart lifts, the back of my neck bristles. It is unrepeatable.

I recalled a conversation with Paul at the open prison. We'd been planning for a few weeks and I thought it time I mentioned Yamilia, surprised that he'd never asked. Perhaps, in his late thirties, he thought a near fifty-year-old wouldn't be bothered with women, or that I was gay, I don't know.

'There's a woman,' I said.

'Oh. Not good.'

'Why?'

He studied me sagely.

'You have a path you want to take. They have a different path. Always. And it's only their path that matters.'

'I see.'

'And they panic. In this business that's not good.'

'This one doesn't panic.'

The very idea seemed alien to him.

We spent many of our days at one of the Playas del Este. They were popular with tourists, but still felt comparatively deserted, so long and wide and plentiful that there was more than enough beach for everyone. I soon took for granted the warm turquoise sea, fine white sand and swaying palms – postcard views. But I didn't lose a cool excitement I never showed; an excitement about the future, about the fact that I was beginning to think that this might actually work out.

Yamilia didn't demand anything, not then; she wasn't

greedy. We already had a TV, so we bought a music system and bootleg CDs. The furnished flat didn't need anything else. When I gave her money for clothes she always bought me something. This was a fresher, easier, safer life for her too and it showed. For a while we both lost a part of us that was manic and possibly self-destructive. Neither of us drank so much. There seemed no need, and, although we still went into Havana regularly, often until the early hours, mostly our weekdays were spent in idleness – in the house, at the beach, the pool – and our evenings with friends or just with each other. I read a great deal and she didn't disturb me, listening to music through headphones or doing something else. She even read herself sometimes, but that was more to impress me; she didn't really have an interest in books, especially fiction – I don't think she saw the point – and was bored by most films too. She appeared rooted in real life, feet on the ground, during those first weeks anyway.

She seemed anxious that I was happy. Cubans are demonstrative, open people. They show their emotions. Although I was very, very happy, unless I was laughing, dancing or in mid-orgasm Yamilia doubted my contentment. I was happy to simply be, didn't feel the need to grin all the time to prove it and am by nature thoughtful anyway, but Yamilia was confused by my occasional silences, mistaking them for unhappiness. She thought sex would cure any moodiness on my part, which was true, but it became exhausting.

José wasn't allowed in the house. He was one of many people who had warned me about Yamilia. Yamilia knew it and wouldn't let him near me. She knew what he knew, whatever that was. I accepted this although I already counted José as a friend, the best I had anyway. And I met him for drinks without her knowledge. He asked about our life and plans, but stayed neutral on the subject of Yamilia; he knew I was beyond any influence. And, like everyone else he knew that association with me was financially life-enhancing, so he played the game.

What neither of them understood was that Yamilia's history was just that, history. Nothing in the past mattered. Even if I heard the very worst and believed it, it made no difference. This was year zero, what mattered was what happened now and from now on; we would succeed or fail on that. Knowing Yamilia and knowing myself, I didn't hold out much hope. I thought from the first meeting that it would end in tears, but so far I didn't regret a minute; I was as happy as I'd ever been – what was there to regret? – Let life do its worst, let fate take its course, let it all end in tears. "Thou blind fool love, what doest thou to mine eyes?" I knew perfectly well what it was doing. I just didn't care.

Many evenings began at Cathedral Square in Old Havana, slowly drinking rum and watching the world go by. It was important to drink slowly, eat occasional snacks and drink water. That way we became slowly mellow as the sun set and day turned into night. The air itself seemed to take on new life as it grew cooler; eager voices, music and expectation came with the darkness. We drew attention from European tourists, often middle-aged women. They gave me darting glances of disapproval, quickly turning away if their stare was returned. It didn't help that Yamilia often looked sixteen. We drew looks from the men too, not moral outrage – just jealousy. It never bothered me, although I was always surprised. If they stayed long enough, they would see us talking, joking, laughing and touching. We were usually like this when life was just life, when history and plans and business didn't intrude. The stares then could become envious and wistful; some would even smile.

Despite not having much skill with the other's language we always talked. Rum improved our conversation. Alcohol breaks down barriers and provides inspiration; it can do that among other things. It's a common notion that all relationships fail first in the bedroom. While there may be some truth in that, I disagree. Relationships fail when people stop communicating. I know people who have been together for years who have no idea what their lover has been doing, thinking or dreaming. Hable con ella. Talk to her.

I didn't always sleep well. It wasn't worry. I felt pretty good. It was more the heat, and then when I did fall into light sleep, the noise – Cuba was rarely silent and I'd come from a quiet country cottage. I read if I wasn't too drunk. Yamilia slept the sleep of the innocent, any place, any time. Well, not quite always. I woke one night to find her fighting somebody or something in her sleep, sometimes clawing, sometimes punching at the air. I rolled her gently onto her side and stroked her hair until she began to snore. I wondered who she was fighting, and hoped it wasn't me.

On another night, as we ate in one of Havana's paladares, entrepreneurial private houses with a licence to serve food, where you ate at small tables in what was, in effect, their front room, I made fun of her and she'd been laughing for hours. She fell off her chair and lay on the floor of the restaurant, holding her stomach as she laughed uncontrollably. We drew stares from the tables around us, which she didn't notice. We set off for a club in Miramar. As I drove along the malecon, she unzipped me and sucked as I drove. It was exciting and wouldn't have taken long, but you can't drive far along the malecon without being required to stop – it's busy: junctions, lights and traffic everywhere. I still regret that I didn't just ignore the lights and risk a massive pile-up. But I moved her and the moment was lost. As I parked by the club Yamilia studied me, and said, quite seriously,

'Did you find that erotique?'

Just a little, Yamilia. Yes, that was erotique.

I liked to think I could dance. On occasions maybe I could. Yamilia stopped once as we were dancing and said with astonishment,

'Your dancing. It is correct!'

But mostly I just jigged about, an approximation of salsa. It didn't matter, nobody cared, certainly not me, and nobody can move like Cubans anyway. I watched my feet as I danced, concentrating on the movement, trying to get the steps right. Dancers in front of me parted and there she was, moving towards me drinks in hand, hair braided with red ribbon, a look in her eyes, mischievous at best, that drew me in. And I was happy with that. Then she smiled, smiled at me, for me and with me. And I was happier still.

Before it got light I drove home or we took a taxi. During a night we drank a couple of bottles between us. There was no staggering, no slurring and no tantrums. I never saw her appear drunk or anything like it, but as soon as we got in the taxi she fell asleep immediately, head lolling from side to side, mouth agape. I carried her into the house, sometimes in my arms, sometimes over my shoulder. I met neighbours on their way to work and we wished each other a pleasant morning. The next day I slept until midday at least. Yamilia was always up early, music blaring, singing while she cleaned the house. Later she took a siesta.

I enjoyed the evenings when people came round. Rosa, if she cooked, brought her son and maybe a friend. Lucia brought her husband, son and daughter and dominated the whole evening, talking about sexo mostly. Her fourteen-year daughter was a promising swimmer and we often went to watch her in competition. The events, which felt like school sport's days to me, were shown on the national news programmes. A bond developed between Lucia and Yamilia. Yamilia was unpopular with many people, but to Lucia she was an entirely natural person, saying and doing what she felt and being exactly what she was. I knew they talked for hours, and I knew they talked about me. Lucia began to take an interest in my health, our love life and our plans. Yamilia, after a few drinks, began to talk about beautiful mulatto children with green eyes. Lucia looked on approvingly. I was being groomed for fatherhood. I didn't find this anything like as disturbing as I'd expected.

Raul checked up on me once a week. A serious man of around thirty, he took my blood pressure, listened to my chest and nagged me about smoking and drinking. He was waiting for documents that would allow him to travel to the USA; he had no patience with Fidel's socialism, earning perhaps fifty dollars a month for his skills, the top wage for skilled professionals. One morning after a check-up we chatted over coffee. He asked how we spent our time, where we went. I told him I'd given some money to a music school and to some young dancers for equipment.

'Why? Do you like ballet?'

'Not really.'

I told him about a programme I'd seen in England about young Cuban musicians, talented but lacking good instruments and dancers who made their own costumes.

'Would you like to go to the theatre, the cinema? Cuba is good for the arts.'

'Yes.'

'Is Yamilia interested?'

'No.'

'I think you should do these things. It would be good for you.'

There was a loud banging at the door. It was Louis, one of Yamilia's uncles. I'd met him briefly. He was a small wiry, light-skinned, muscular man, a gardener for Havana's parks. He immediately began to plead with me in agitated Spanish. As I closed the door and walked back into the room he followed me closely, clearly under the impression that I had a clue what he was saying. I looked to Raul for help.

'He says Yamilia is a thief. He says Yamilia bought him a TV and now she has taken it away. It was his TV and she has taken it.'

'Why did she take it?' I said.

Louis waved his arms frantically as he shouted, veins pumping on his neck and forehead. He must have come from Havana to see me and the sweaty, tiring journey hadn't lessened his anger. I visited his flat once. He was in his forties with a young wife and baby. The flat was bare and a bit depressing; life a struggle. I could imagine how a new TV would be welcome. Although I was made welcome, his wife didn't disguise her low opinion of Yamilia. I wondered if she was the catalyst for this. Raul continued to translate.

'She took it and gave it to them, he says.'

'Who are they?'

'That family.'

'What family?'

'The family of Lazaro...'

Louis interrupted us with something Raul couldn't translate. We searched for a dictionary. He found what he was looking for and jabbed a finger at the word.

'He says Yamilia is a shameless woman.'

He was too angry to make sense, shouting, his face too close to mine. Any sympathy I had evaporated and I asked him to leave. He was shocked and deflated, unable to fathom why this clear injustice had failed to move me.

'Tell him I'm sorry about his TV,' I said to Raul, 'maybe I can do something for him later.'

Louis nodded, unconvinced, his pride hurt at being dismissed.

'And tell him I like shameless women.'

'What was all that about?' I asked.

Raul spread his arms wide.

'A misunderstanding maybe. I don't know. He didn't make much sense.'

He asked what I knew about Louis. I told him about my visit.

'The TV would be a big thing for him. You have introduced money into a small world of people. Yamilia's life is changed. She can help some of her family, but not everyone. The longer you are here the more people will know of you. Most Cubans will take you as you are. If you offer something they may take it or they may not. Money makes a difference though, Chris, and many people know you are here. You are here for yourself, but you must be careful of the effect you can have on other people. There are bad people everywhere. You will be bored with me telling you but you must be careful, of your health and the people around you.'

He surprised me by asking for a beer. I had the same out of respect; he'd warned me that rum would ruin my health.

'I can understand why you have come here. Cuba is hard for Cubans, but not so much for you. If you are clever you can do what you like. Women are more available to you here. I think you should slow down, learn a bit more, speak Spanish and see what is possible for you. What you do, the clubs, dancing and drinking, I can see why in the beginning, but now, why? You are an intelligent man; there is more than that for you here.'

'And Yamilia?'

'I like Yamilia. I like both of you. You need people around you who will help you. You are vulnerable until your Spanish improves, until you understand more about life here.' He flashed a rare smile, 'Take it easy, slow down and enjoy your life. Thanks for the beer.'

If you don't make mistakes, you aren't really trying.
Coleman Hawkins

MAGIC NIGHT

A few days later we went to Havana to meet some 'good friends'. Yamilia said I would have a good time. The taxi dropped us by the Ambos Mundos.

'We will take a bicycle taxi from here,' she said.

The fat man waited by the hotel. We often used his taxi. Bicycle taxis are a quicker way of negotiating Old Havana's narrow back streets. A CD player was attached to the handle bars and he listened to music constantly. Enormous, black, very smiley and friendly, he'd been pedalling tourists around Havana for years, which was desperately hard work. I wondered why he hadn't either lost weight or had a heart attack.

The journey lasted a few minutes. We stopped at a semi-decrepit, tall grey building and paid our panting, sweating driver. Yamilia, small and nervous in the dark deserted street, phoned ahead. We climbed the steps to a third floor flat and were welcomed by a tall, grey-haired man in his fifties at the top, Lazaro. He took both my hands in his, pressed them together as though we were both at prayer, nodded and bowed obsequiously. He held my hands for far too long, muttering greetings in Spanish as though I was a visiting dignitary. He led us along a landing to an open door and into a room with a sofa and a few chairs. We were directed to the sofa. He introduced his family: his wife, blonde and glaring, and Amado, his son, fidgeting restlessly in an armchair, sighing loudly, running his fingers through his long gelled hair, impatiently and pointedly not acknowledging me. Only Yamilia and Lazaro were smiling. This was a fine social gathering and we were all having a splendid time.

The usual artificial flowers and some travel posters added some colour to the flat. Why, with the abundance of real and beautiful plants everywhere, did they persist with the synthetic? Perhaps it was the struggle to keep them alive and the constant rationing of water. Lazaro placed a bottle of Silver Dry on the table next to me. He opened it, tipped some into the corner of the room for their saints and poured me a glass. I gestured for him to take some and he thanked me at length as though I were the host offering my own drinks. Amado declined, his skin jumping with energy and impatience. He ran out of places to look to avoid looking at me, sighed heavily, pushed himself out of the chair and stomped to the back of the house.

Lazaro offered us slices of cold pork from a large flower-patterned plate. When we had taken a slice each he put the plate next to the rum, indicating that it was only for us. I was ill at ease and the general atmosphere was tense. His wife clearly thought that wasting food that cost a week's wages on me was not a good idea and, although Lazaro might be welcoming me to their home, she didn't.

If these were people I was supposed to meet it wasn't going very well. I couldn't believe that Yamilia thought I'd be so naive, that I wouldn't see through this, but she was a different person here, nervous and restrained. She touched my arm,

'The magic show will be here soon.'

A skinny young man arrived with a holdall. He had a boyish, pale face that emphasised red lips. His hands were delicate, feminine, with long thin fingers. He wore a red jacket and black trousers with thick shiny seams, a white shirt with black bow tie: The Magic Man. Over the next hour he performed tricks and illusions that were the equal of anything I'd seen from overhyped magicians on TV. He made things appear and disappear. He did unfathomable card tricks, he even produced a white dove – I can't explain how. Yamilia clapped and squealed, Lazaro nodded and smiled, adding the odd 'bravo'. Wife stood and glowered from the kitchen doorway. Amado didn't appear. I clapped along too and tried to show some appreciation. Where did he come from? Was he a friend? Had they hired him? I admired, but did not enjoy, one second of it.

I didn't want to offer him money, but thought I should at least make a show. I took out my wallet and fiddled with it. Roberto leapt up and pushed my hand back to my pocket, backed away in his prayer mode again, bowing and scraping.

'No, Chris,' said Yamilia, 'is not necessary.'

I asked for the bathroom. As is often the case in Cuban houses the bathroom was reached through a bedroom. Lazaro pointed the way. I walked through a darkened room. Returning, I passed Amado sprawled across a bed, fully dressed. I stopped and watched him. He snorted an abrupt piggy snore, one of his legs twitched and he farted. I'd had enough.

'Yamilia, I have to leave,' I said.

'But Chris, we have more food for you.'

I didn't like the 'we'. I stood up. Wife snorted from the doorway and turned into her kitchen. Lazaro stood, his grey eyes showing an anger that didn't spread to his face. He spoke softly to Yamilia in Spanish. I understood him say that it was all right, maybe I was tired, we would do this another time. He led us back along the landing. At the top of the stairs I shook his hand, said my thanks and apologised for leaving early. He grasped my hand again in both his and spoke; he was taller than me, a big man, so he stood on a lower step, enabling him to look up. I didn't understand a word. I met his eyes and didn't like what I saw, trying not to breathe in his cologne, a sweet, sickly scent. Yamilia stood a few steps down, watching from the shadows. I released my hand from his grip and joined her, but he followed me down, this time taking my hands more firmly. He turned and moved to a lower step so that he again looked up, and spoke softly, hypnotically, almost in a whisper, his tone polite, his demeanour respectful, and the danger unmistakeable.

Without looking for a taxi we walked back to Old Havana in silence, keeping to the middle of the street, as most Cubans did – people had died when pieces of masonry fell away from the crumbling buildings. After a few paces Yamilia stopped. I turned to look at her, a solitary figure in the deserted, unlit street, the glow of her white satin dress giving her a ghostly appearance.

'Chris, I no understand you. You have twenty year more than me, you have much experience, what you want?'

She stamped a foot on the cobbled street, nearly toppling off her high-heels. The bad feeling in my gut melted away and I felt only the need to protect her, alone in the dark of a Havana backstreet. A tiny, beautiful woman who had come to the big city when she was fifteen years old. And she'd out-toughed everybody. It had taken its toll on her, but her spirit was not broken. She stood here, nakedly honest now and she was exasperated with me. But I was alone too. I was exasperated too. What the fuck had all that been about? Did Yamilia know? Did she understand? Was it all out of her control and so out of her mind too? I didn't know and right now I didn't care. There would be no answers from her tonight; I would have to figure this out myself. I walked back and put my arms round her, pulled her to me. I waited as she relaxed into me.

'I don't want to go home yet, let's go and get a drink somewhere.'

Outside the Ambos Mundos the fat man waited for more passengers. He called us over, invited us to listen to some music. It was reggae; he was a connoisseur and had cassettes from all over the world given to him by his passengers. We listened, allowing the music to change our mood. I asked him if he would like to join us for a drink.

'Where?

'In here,' I said, pointing to the hotel.

'It's not possible for me.'

'It's possible,' I said.

The fat man told stories of his passengers. Yamilia, happy again, laughed easily at his dry delivery. He told us about the 'Lord' who came to Cuba every year and always used his bicycle taxi.

'A Lord?' I said.

'Yes, an English Lord, from London.'

'What is his name?'

'Lord Chelsea,' he said.

I explained to Yamilia what a Lord was.

'And he comes every year?'

'Yes, sometime more. He comes for more than ten year. Always use my taxi.'

'Where does he stay?'

'The Inglaterra, always.'

'You sure he is a Lord?'

He stiffened a little at my doubt, fiddled among some crumpled cards in his wallet and handed me a plain white card with black type: Lord Chelsea, Financial Services and Expertise, followed by an address in the Fulham Road, probably a PO Box. I thought, 'con man' and nodded thoughtfully and respectfully as I handed it back.

'How old is he?'

'Seventy-six. He is a Lord, a very respectful man. Beautiful clothes. He pay me very well.'

'And,' I said, 'when he comes now, does he like the Cuban women?'

'Yes, I take him in my taxi.'

'And do you take him many times?'

'Every day,' he said proudly, 'every day.'

The next day Yamilia said she needed to go to Havana for

a manicure. While I was in no doubt she would return with pristine painted nails, the momentarily averted eyes didn't ease the bad feeling I'd woken with. I felt Lazaro's grey eyes still boring into me, his sickly scent lingered in my nostrils. I dropped her in Old Havana and had coffee in the Ambos Mundos. Lazaro was on my mind, but not in any way I could deal with or shake off. How could I deal with it? I didn't know what had happened.

I walked to the malecon, climbed onto the thick seawall. The sun, not yet strong, was hidden intermittently behind wispy, white clouds darting east to west. My head spun, doubts stabbed at my gut. I walked along the wall for a mile or so with the wind at my back, then turned and walked back into it. My head slowly cleared, the worry vanished. The wind blew it all away.

I sat on the wall watching lithe, shouting children, white through black, play baseball with a broom handle and a ball made of tape on the wide pavement. Behind them on the balconies across the street drying clothes fluttered like flags of all nations. An ancient red and white Chevrolet pulled over to the kerb, its engine roaring, groaning under the strain of a thousand loving retunes, services and home-made parts. But its paintwork gleamed proudly and its chrome sparkled in the sun proclaiming 'They don't make them like me anymore.' The young driver leaned out of the window,

'¿Taxi, senor?'

I smiled and shook my head. He smiled back, waved and gunned the Maquina, Yank Tank, into action and merged slowly, noisily back into the traffic with a clunking of gears as the engine, over seventy years old, dutifully groaned into another day's service. This strange, beautiful city was my home and that was enough. Whatever happened I would deal with it.

I walked up to central Havana and the park, but away from the sea it was hot and sweaty, time for a cool drink. Several large tourist hotels surrounded the park. From the Plaza Hotel on the corner of Neptuno and Zuleta came the thin murmur and tinkle of an indoor fountain. Inside I hit a natural, airy, high ceilinged coolness and sat down to the ring of glasses on tables and laughter. The reassuring chatter of female voices greeted me when I phoned Yamilia. Her nails were done.

'Meet me at the Plaza.'

I sat transfixed as an English football match played on a large screen, stared like a man deprived. It felt good to sit in cool surroundings and watch football, take an interest in the game and the result. Two plump Irishmen sat at the table next to me, shouting at the TV. The match ended and another was scheduled to begin later.

In their mid-thirties with round sunburnt faces, Tom and Liam had just returned from Santiago de Cuba.

'Some of the poverty there was disgusting,' said Tom, 'time for another revolution.'

'Maybe,' I said, 'but I love it here.'

'Oh, right, don't get me wrong mate. Cracking country, cracking people. But this Marxist shit, what's in it for the people? You've got doctors and scientists driving taxis and waiting tables to make ends meet. Good idea in the first place, don't get me wrong mate, kicking out the fucking Americans, or should I say the fucking mafia? Viva Che and all that. But it's all gone to shit. It's bollocks. Patria o muerte for fuck's sake. Country or death. How about a decent standard of living before we start talking about dying for the fucking country?'

I told them I was getting out of Havana for a while.

'Vinales, Pinar del Rio mate,' said Liam, 'that's the place, not too far, lovely mountains, rivers and lakes. Beaches too if you're not sick of them. Fucking gorgeous.'

I heard a soft rustle of silk behind me. Yamilia had a bought a new dress. She loved white silk or satin or linen. She gave a twirl,

'You like?'

'That's great, love,' said Tom, 'that's just the thing.'

She stared at them with open curiosity. I gave her money for some more drinks. Tom and Liam were silent for a couple of minutes while they reappraised the situation, watching me. Was I now one of the reasons there should be another revolution?

'Jesus, it's fucking Arsenal now,' said Liam, snapping back to life.

'So what do you do in England, mate?' said Tom.

'I live here.'

'Fucking hell, which version of the lottery did you win? Divorced?'

I nodded. Yamilia returned with the drinks.

'That's a fucking racket too, eh mate? You get their knickers and they get your house and car. Fucking racket it is. Why do we do it, mate, eh, why do we do it?'

I laughed. Tom glanced at Yamilia, who smiled at him, answering his question. She had forgotten her nails and her new dress. She'd missed the sentiment, but recognised some of the words and she'd noticed the accent.

'Where are these men from?'

'Ireland, darling,' said Liam.

'¿Donde Ireland?' Where is it?'

I drew a crude Britain shape in the spilt water on the table top with another smaller splodge off to the left. She nodded.

'And is English too?'

'It's complicated, love,' said Tom.

'You speak different,' she said.

'That we do.'

We left them and went to eat.

'We're going to Pinar del Rio tomorrow,' I said.

'¿Porque?' Why?

'Aburrido.' Bored.

'OK.'

The province of Pinar del Rio is west of Havana, a few hours' drive. We had intended to visit the capital of the same name, but stopped in the town of Vinales because I liked its wooden colonnades and red tiled roofs. We ate overlooking the main square with its unused looking church as night drew in.

'Where we stay? Here?'

'Let's find a hotel.'

'But I can't stay in hotel, Chris. I tell you before, is impossible for me.'

It was illegal for Cubans to stay in tourist hotels, one of many reasons why Tom and Liam had a point. I checked our guide. A few miles from town was a ranch complex with twenty cabins.

'Yes, you can,' I said.

I parked by reception to investigate. It was a modern tourist complex. The cabins had showers, satellite TV, air-conditioning, balconies with spectacular views and hot tubs. There were restaurants, bars, a swimming pool, health spa, warm sulphurous baths, mud baths, massage, physiotherapy, acupuncture, digitopuncture (whatever that was), medical checkups and more. The price included three meals a day and *all drinks*. I didn't care what Yamilia thought or what the law of the land was. We were staying here. I left Yamilia in the car and established that rooms were available. One young woman, Celia according to her name tag, tended reception.

'How long would you like to stay?'

Four nights I thought, maybe more. I glanced at the price list, casually studied my wad of cash as I appeared to think about it.

'Only you?' she said.

'No, I have someone with me.'

I fetched Yamilia from the car. She looked around.

'No, Chris. We can't stay here.'

'Yes, we can.'

Celia's face fell with embarrassment.

'I am very sorry, sir. But we can't allow it.'

Yamilia gave me her *I told you so* glare. I placed two fifty dollar bills on the desk. Celia didn't acknowledge them, just studied us as she considered. Leaving the money she walked over to a tall, name-tagged black man in an expensive dark suit. Slick and sleek with sunglasses despite the lack of sun, he stood in the centre of the lobby looking casually authoritative, surveying his domain. They spoke for several minutes, he occasionally pointed his sunglasses at us as he listened, frequently shaking his head. But it was a long, drawn-out refusal. Celia returned.

'I'm sorry. It is not possible.'

I laid three more fifties on the desk. She nodded to her manager, who walked briskly to us and shook my hand. He kissed Yamilia's cheek.

'I am Ôscar, your manager. You can park your car over there. I will send someone for your bags. Celia will take care of you now. I hope you have a wonderful stay.'

He leaned over the desk, took the top four notes and walked away. I put my passport on top of the remaining fifty. Celia picked it up.

We were in a valley of steep limestone mountains topped with pines. In the flat valleys farmers grew tobacco, fruits and vegetables. On one of our rare treks we found a high waterfall and swam for hours without seeing another person. I settled into a routine of breakfast, swim, massage, siesta, evening meal and drinks on our balcony or in the hot tub on the back terrace. Yamilia did much the same except she took every health and beauty treatment going. The place seemed to slow Yamilia's metabolism. I was happy to at last slow her down in bed, tired of the pounding, sweaty, biting, scratching and relentlessly energetic sex that seemed to be the norm here. I think the enjoyment of slowness was a new and novel experience for her; she smiled at herself in the mirror, made no attempt to speed things up, allowing herself to be led to whatever happened next. In the mornings she bounced around like a child.

I decided not to mention Lazaro. She had an immediate and effective defence mechanism against enquiry anyway – anger. That didn't mean I couldn't still read the signs, which were often obvious. But this was the *big* thing, apart from money, of course. This was the invisible but malignant *thing* that threatened our relationship so far. And for the key to that there were no signs, no slips. I wouldn't find it. I'd just win her away from it. I thought I wanted that.

She became more affectionate: a touch on my arm, a stroke of my neck and spontaneous broad smiles. You're not as hard as you think, I thought. The last night we sat on our balcony watching the stars. We had made love and were sharing a bottle of rum. We wouldn't finish it. Healthy living made us tired earlier; we would drink two or three glasses and fall into bed. My arm was resting on the wooden table between us. Music floated faintly up from the club below, late night swimmers laughed in the pool. She stroked the back of my hand.

'Chris,' she said.

'¿Si?'

'You want get married?'

And what is bettre than wisedom? Womman. And what is bettre than a good womman? Nothyng.
Chaucer

PERFECT WOMEN

While Yamilia showered I sat listening to music, half dozing, still in rubbery, sleepy mode from our break. I heard her move to the kitchen, slamming cupboard doors and talking to herself. She marched into the room, stomping on the tiled floor. Normally she was light on her feet, I wouldn't hear her coming, now every step echoed. She was naked, her black curly hair, still wet, snaked around her head, face and shoulders. She moved to the coffee table, bent over in front of me, took out a cigarette and lit it. After a couple of deep drags she pointed it at me, her eyes darting and restless.

'You want perfect woman, you go to Havana,' she said.

I wondered what she meant by perfect woman. I wondered who this perfect woman was and why I was supposed to want her. I wondered where this was going. I decided not to speak until I knew. And then be very careful what I said. She stomped back to the kitchen.

'Many beautiful women in Havana,' she said, to herself. She turned in the doorway and stood glaring at me. She cupped her small breasts in her hands.

'You want them big here? Go to Havana. Many women in Havana big here. You want perfect ass?'

She turned round, showing me her perfect ass. I didn't say anything. She returned to the table, stubbed out her cigarette, then immediately reached for another. She bent from the waist, legs slightly apart and made a fuss of lighting it, manically flicking the lighter and showing the diamond shape between the tops of her thighs and her bottom, her smooth little cunt peeped out at me. I sighed and adjusted myself in my shorts. She turned and shouted at me.

'You want perfect body, you go to Havana.'

There's no such thing as a perfect woman or a perfect body. Whatever minor flaws she had were part of her, and made her what she was, and the way she moved, and everything else I liked and didn't want to analyse. She knew I loved her, I was sure. But today it was obviously not enough; she was having a crisis of confidence. She stood at the open window. Some boys in the street stopped and stared up at her. She didn't see them, smoking furiously and muttering to herself.

'You have the eyes of young man, big heart. You have power and money in Cuba. Age is not important here. Many women in Havana want man like you.'

She turned and shouted at me again.

'You want perfect woman.'

She nodded to herself in agreement.

'OK. Take perfect woman. Go to Havana.'

She set off for the kitchen again as though it was all

decided; as though I'd rejected her and was about to pack my bags for Havana. She threw her cigarette in the sink and stared out of the window. Her hair had dried in the heat, wild, sticking to her back, neck and cheeks and jutting out at all angles. I moved behind her and put my arms around her waist, tried to hug her without making her aware of my erection. I stood awkwardly, slightly sideways.

'I'm not interested in the women in Havana, Yamilia.'

She let out a small sigh and seemed to shrink in front of me. She stood on tiptoe, hands gripping the edge of the sink, knuckles white. She gave me a brief sideways glance. Some of the tension slipped away. She wasn't finished though.

'I see you look at the women in Havana. The woman from the ballet. She is beautiful and muy intelligente. She likes you. She can dance, speak English, she have money. You can have woman like this.'

'You think so?'

'I think so.'

'But I haven't.'

'¿Que?'

'I haven't got a woman like that. I've got you, because that's what I want. That's why I came here. For you. I don't want that woman. I want you.'

She shrank further, became smaller. She'd sensed my stiffy, despite my efforts to hide it, and was backing into me. She took a deep breath and sighed. I gathered her tangled hair, moved it from her face and spread it down her back.

'Is true?'

'Is true.'

Her face collapsed into a broad smile. She spun round and kissed me, and in the same moment pulled down my shorts, tried to get down on her knees. I pulled her up.

'No. Not now. We're going out. Get ready, you look a mess.'

'Mess?'

'Si. Fayo. Muy, muy fayo.' Very, very ugly.

We went to the Nacional. I didn't like it much, but this was a treat and I could hardly take her to one of the paladares or peso bars that I preferred. She spent two hours getting ready, her hair tied back tight and close to her scalp like a flamenco dancer, set off with a mariposa and dark red lipstick. She wore a long silk dress; almost see through, but not quite. And high-heels. She could barely walk in them, she never could, always breaking or falling off them. She drew looks from everyone, which I suppose was the general idea. I liked being with her like that of course. I liked the jealous looks from the men, but it wasn't the way I liked Yamilia. She was like a doll, not quite real. I preferred her in jeans and a t-shirt. I didn't tell her that. You don't tell a woman who's spent two hours getting ready that you prefer the casual look.

It wasn't quite stuffy in the hotel dining room, not the stuffy of similar places in Europe or the USA, but it was stuffy for Cuba. The air-conditioning hid the smell of cigar smoke, but the band, the music, never quite allowed stuffiness, always the feeling that a fiesta might break out any moment despite the exalted company, the white table cloths, the art and the large ornate mirrors. She ordered too much food as always, couldn't make up her mind what to have, ordered everything she liked and couldn't eat a quarter of it. She didn't change her behaviour in the stiff atmosphere; she didn't change her behaviour for anybody. The waiters were Cuban, like her, and she spoke to them as she spoke to everybody. She was rude. As we ate she scanned the room, gossiped and criticised the diners, pointed out minor politicians, drug dealers, Hollywood satyrs, pimps and whores.

'You want buy house?' she said.

We'd been here before. Eventually I wanted a house, but not yet. I hadn't figured out who everyone was, who I could trust. My Spanish wasn't good enough. I smiled, today was a good day and I didn't want to spoil it.

'You've seen a house?'

She put down her knife and fork to concentrate her power towards me, the pupils of her eyes widened and flashed like cat on the prowl as she saw her chance.

'In Guanabacoa. Good house, old, colonial, high roof, beautiful floors and big patio. Is good house on the street but have bars on windows, long way back in garden – tranquila, cool inside. Mucho calor outside, is cool in house. Big wood doors, two doors together all blue, like the sea. Is beautiful house. You like this house.'

I was in a good mood, soft and happy. She must have known she would wear me down.

'Casa azul,' I said.

'Si, a blue house.'

'OK. Show me the house.'

She beamed a huge and happy smile at me. As we left she asked for a bag for the uneaten food. The people at the nearby tables looked at us in amazement, perhaps disgust. As I drove home I became aroused at the prospect of the night ahead. She gazed through her window at a full moon, a perfect grey flecked disc floating above an inky sea, a silver light shimmering across the calm surface towards us, trailing us. Without turning her head she reached over and laid her hand in my lap.

'Much work for him tonight,' she said.

The next day we took a taxi to Guanabacoa, a rough colonial town a few miles away. The house had big, blue, arched double-doors and barred windows. It was empty so we peered though the bars at a large, high ceilinged reception room and a doorway through to the rest of the house. Way back I could see a kitchen and a patio. Back there the noise from the street would be dulled. The floors were a patchwork of coloured tiles. I liked it immediately.

'Who owns it?' I said.

'People who move to Spain.'

'How much?'

'Nueve-mil. Nine-thousand dollars.'

I liked it but I was content with life as it was. A house would need to be furnished and it was illegal for me to own property in Cuba; my name could never be on the papers. I didn't want to make that commitment yet. I loved Yamilia but I didn't trust her. There was no advantage for me, it could only benefit her. Maybe after a year or so. Yamilia had begun to talk about business, not in any interested way, just that my money (and she didn't know how much) would only last so long. There should be an income from a business of some kind. I did have plans with Paul, but I hadn't told her. There were lots of opportunities. And

I'd need help. José was no use here; he was small-time in her opinion. I needed to meet people. I needed to move up a level.

Back at the flat Yamilia cooked. She was a good cook, a talent she rarely practised – probably wise, lest I got too used to it.

'You like house?' she said as we ate.

'Si, but not now.'

'¿Porqué?'

'It will take time to get the money. And it's too fast for me. I want to think about it.'

'OK.'

Work like you don't need the money. Love like you've never been hurt. Dance like nobody's watching.
Satchel Paige

TONY

'With business you will need help. It will be too difficult for you alone. No Spanish, you don't understand what happens here.'

Yamilia had little interest in business beyond her own needs, but she saw clearly, before me, that I'd get nowhere without serious help. Parties, bars and clubs had introduced me to dozens of people, some of them useful, but if I took them on I would have an army of gofers. Nobody could take me beyond street level. If I wanted to make money, I was looking in the wrong places.

So I met Tony. Tony could fix everything for the house in Guanabacoa if I decided to buy it. He was an important man; he had houses all over Havana. He had served in the army, had worked high up in the system. He knew how everything worked. I needed someone like him; I would get nowhere with people like José.

'How do you know this man?' I said.

Her eyes slid away.

'He is tio, uncle, of someone I know. He want to help you.'

I made a show of seriously considering this. Everybody wanted to help me.

'The tio of Amado?' I said.

She rolled her eyes at the stupidity of that idea.

'OK,' I said, 'we can meet; see what he has to say.'

'And Chris,' she said, holding my eyes this time.

'Si?'

'Tony no like people who drink.'

He came to the flat the next day. I was showered and sharp, only mildly hung over.

'So Tony never drinks,' I said.

'Maybe a beer.'

She said this in an unusually respectful tone. How well did she know him? There was no point in asking. She was nervous, watching from the window while we waited. When she saw his car she watched through the spy hole until she saw him reach us and opened the door. I thought she should have let him knock. They greeted each other Cuban style, like long-lost friends, all smiles and kisses. He towered above her, out of breath from the stairs. Smiling and laughing he came to me hand outstretched, a huge hand gripped mine and cut off my circulation.

'Mucho gustar, Chrees, mucho gustar. Como esta?'

'Mucho gustar, Tony, muy bien.'

'Bien, bien.'

He was laughing, nervously I thought, but it was a natural sound, big and booming as if he liked to laugh and did it often.

'Tony speak no English, Chris, you want coffee?'

I looked at Tony.

'You want coffee, Tony? Beer, rum, freco?'

71

'Cervesa, por favor, gracias.'

I went into the kitchen. As Yamilia took beer from the fridge I poured a large rum. Despite his lack of English we got by. He spoke very slowly and expressively, using his arms, hands, smiles and frowns. I can understand a lot of Spanish if it's spoken slowly. Yamilia stayed close, listening and occasionally translating. He liked to talk, much of it conversational rather than business, as he spoke of a Cuba the brochures don't advertise.

In his late fifties, Tony was a jovial, well-fed giant of a man. Despite an impressive stomach drooping over his belt he looked fit and vital, had a full head of thick, silver hair brushed back from his face and forehead, piercing green eyes above a Roman nose and almost feminine, sensuous lips. Beneath the smiles and bonhomie was a definite authority though – I didn't want this man as an enemy. He'd fallen out of love with the revolution years before and made his way with whatever opportunities arose, which particularly since the Russians left in 1989, I gathered came mainly from tourism. He thought things were slowly changing for the better; this was a good time for business opportunities in Cuba. He could arrange the purchase of the house. He had other ideas: cars were mentioned, and antiques; I thought he could help with most lines of business.

I was aware that his income probably came from fleecing rather than helping people like me – he'd add as much as he could to prices for services provided, see how soft I was. But there was something about him I liked: warmth, humour, a weary wisdom – I wasn't sure – just a vague connection, however small that I might be able to trust, to work on. He smiled. Yamilia smiled.

'OK,' I said, 'we'll talk again.'

We parted agreeing on a meal in the near future, where presumably something would be decided.

While Yamilia slept I called Paul. The early hours, particularly four or five in the morning, were perfect for catching people in England at the start of their day. I drank rum and kept an increasingly eccentric diary as I waited.

'I've met someone who could be useful.'

'Do we need anybody? Can't we do this ourselves?'

'We need somebody.'

'Hmm.'

'How's England?'

'I'm still tagged. I see Tony fucking Blair's grinning face every day. It's wet, it's grey and it's cold. The whole country has foot and mouth disease. I'm pissed off. How's Cuba?'

'Yamilia wants to buy a house.'

'How much?'

'Nine thousand.'

'Do it.'

'This person I've met, Tony, he can sort out the purchase.'

'He'll rob you.'

'They all will, up to a point.'

'You can't do it without him?'

'I wouldn't know where to start. You still interested in the business here?'

'Absolutely. I've joined Cuba Solidarity and The Friends of Cuba. There's no extradition. And most of their banking is still on paper. It sounds wonderful. I've been talking to some friends in the city. They think the Cuba tourism thing could work. I'll get the customers with money and you show them Cuba, the Cuba the tourists don't see. I just think we would be better doing it ourselves. Do we have to involve Pedro?'

'Tony.'

'Whatever.'

'Yes, we do. It's different here. Everything is different. Nothing is as it seems. And my Spanish is terrible. We need help.'

'OK. Oh, I've applied for an ABTA. I'm forging the documents as we speak. Fourteen grand.'

'Use my Amex card.'

'No, I'm using one of your remaining accounts before it dries up. Can't explain here. Got other plans for the card.'

'Meet anyone at Cuba Solidarity?'

'Lots of rosy glassed *Guardian* types, beards. Some nice women though, it's good fun.'

'I gave some money to a ballet company here.'

'Why?'

'I wanted to. It can't harm my image.'

'Hmm.'

'How's life as a free man? Are you drinking again?'

'Moderately.'

'OK. No more mistakes.'

'Absolutely.'

I knew of two of Paul's arrests. One at a petrol station where he was so drunk he pulled the wrong card from his wallet and another at a Leeds hotel where, after a week's residence, he forgot who he was on leaving and checked out under a different name. A clever man, but three years of his life in prison through drunkenness. I wondered for the first time if he'd do it again, and if he'd take me with him.

Love, as I have heard say, wears spectacles, through which copper looks like gold, rags like rich apparel, and specks in the eye like pearls.
Sancho Panza: Don Quixote

CAMAGUEY

Just when I expected Yamilia to continue the pressure, she announced that she was bored with Havana and suggested another trip to her mother's in Camaguey. I assumed her mother had phoned. We hadn't been there since the trip over a year before.

We set off early, but were still two hours short when darkness fell. In Cuba half the vehicles drive without lights and many of the drivers are drunk. There are donkeys, goats, cows, dogs, pedestrians, jay-walkers, drunks, bicycles, motorbikes and children playing – mostly in unlit streets. Ancient lorries belch black smoke at every gear change. Overtaking could result in a cloud of toxic, foul-smelling fumes puffed through the open window – not good for a hangover. More than once I was forced onto the verge, steering a fine line between clipping an oncoming lorry or mowing down pedestrians. Yamilia showed no concern – just an everyday hazard.

'They don't care,' she said.

Long stretches of almost deserted motorway were punctuated with men, women and children selling bunches of bananas, onions and other assorted farm produce. They walked to the middle of the road waving their stuff. The campesinos, farmers, I'd met, mostly in small towns and villages seemed happy enough, poor but not really lacking anything. But to stand in the hot sun all day on the slim chance of making a few pesos spoke of hardship I hadn't encountered. And in the country it was everywhere.

In the nineteenth century it was possible to ride the length of Cuba without leaving the shade of trees. Sugar plantations changed that. Although there are now protected forest areas and a burgeoning eco-tourism, large stretches were fairly dull and treeless. Life in the country was controlled chaos. The working day was long, with a strange selection of archaic vehicles chugging back and forth, sometimes pulling trailers full of people. An abiding memory, especially travelling, was the long lines of Cubans everywhere, all over the country, waiting for a non-existent bus, or a lift from a friendly face, or for a price they could afford, or crammed into the back of lorries, standing room only. Havana to Camaguey took twenty hours that way, with a few rest stops. I watched all this from the comfort of my air-conditioned car, or as I walked past long queues and into dollar shops, or as I entered clubs and hotels barred to Cubans – always accepted politely with no outward signs of resentment. And there were times when, for all my enjoyment, I thought Tom and Liam were right: time for another revolution. And, but for the police, the military, maybe, but José had said support for Fidel was strongest here, in the country among the campesinos, eighty per cent, only the cities held pockets of resentment.

Signs for the revolution were everywhere, mostly colourful and vaguely inspiring. Che's face stared angelically, heroically out of many; few showed Fidel. Secure in his stature he hasn't made an icon of himself, no statues, no boasting, no glorifying of his name. That will come after his death. As he says: History will absolve me. We will see. Occasionally the signs were comically old-fashioned and Soviet in nature. A board outside an ancient, toxic cement factory proclaimed to its workers and passersby that they should 'Work Ideologically', a relic of Russian influence, Stalinist and incongruous among the palm trees. Nobody took any notice of it. Cubans work to survive, just like anybody else.

Although he had no licence I was glad to hand the car keys to Fifi when we arrived. We were given the main bedroom where her mother and Sally usually slept, while they moved to a smaller room. They cooked over a charcoal grill, drew water from a well in the garden and showered and flushed the toilet with buckets of water. I adjusted to this, as I had on the previous visit, almost immediately. Life changed in the country. Although there is always a sense of community, even in the most deprived and run down areas of Havana, it is much more evident here, with its base in farming – the campesinos. Apart from the young and those fat on Florida dollars, support for Fidel was common though not unanimous, the economy one of barter as much as money.

My money bought food and rum and new visitors to

the house. We brought the music system with us so her mother had to suffer fiestas on most nights. The visitors brought the first signs of friction here. Yamilia spoke to me in the garden. Not all the visitors were friends; she didn't even know some of them. They were enjoying the hospitality my money provided. I must tell them they were not welcome. I had no idea if they were welcome or not and didn't much care, but her face was hard; she didn't like to see me taken advantage of. I must do something about it. I saw her point. Life is difficult in Cuba; you helped friends if you could, but you didn't throw money at strangers.

When the usual drinkers arrived she pointed out the culprits. I met them at the gate while she watched. No party tonight, boys, we're taking it easy, see you around. They reacted to my terrible Spanish and English diplomacy with typical Cuban equanimity. No problem, smiles, friendly pats on the back and they ambled away. Hasta luego. I walked back past Yamilia. She watched me as I passed. Settled, but not emphatic enough. No indignant offence on my part, no permanent banishment. Was this Englishman a soft touch?

I liked to sit on the front porch and read. I had an ancient copy of *Plutarch's Lives*, one of the few books in English I managed to find at the bookstalls in the Plaza Armas before we left. It was pleasantly entertaining, particularly the lives of Caesar, Antony, Pompeii and Cleopatra. The sort of book I had neither the patience nor time to read in England – on a lazy afternoon in a rocking chair on the porch it came alive. I put the book down to light a cigarette. Yamilia picked it up and flicked though it, stopping at an illustration. She asked what it was. I explained that Cleopatra, imperious and reclining, was experimenting with poisons. A slave writhed in agony at her feet while she considered her choice, another, dead, was being carried off. She studied the picture with fascination and no little enthusiasm, smiled beautifully and walked away.

We could get rum at any time. All over Cuba there are bars in the middle of nowhere, open twenty-four hours. Presumably subsidised, they serve the local population: farmers, drivers, lost souls – anyone who needs a drink. We were served by such a bar halfway between Lugareno and Camaguey, where Fifi drove for supplies.

Later we stayed at a hotel in Camaguey for three days, as a break from the fiestas and to give her mother a rest. I realised how little we were alone and how well we got on together when we managed it. I paid an extra hundred dollars to the hotel for Yamilia to stay with me. The one ATM we found wasn't working so I got cash from a bank in the main square. During the inevitable wait I surveyed the bank, idly wondering how you would go about robbing it. An armed doorman allowed only a few people in the bank at any time. While we waited a van delivered or took away cash, I wasn't sure which. Three khaki uniformed guards armed with pistols and shotguns oversaw the process, constantly alert and suspicious. If you managed to get past them the usual tourist police stood on every street corner. And then where? No borders to cross, nowhere to hide from prying eyes or the CDR. Any sudden riches would be noted and need to be accounted for. Leave the country? They would catch you at the airports if you missed a traffic fine. The only way, if you were mad enough to attempt it, would be to kill anyone in your path and take a fast boat to Miami. Chances of success? Almost nil. Penalty for failure. Life in prison or, more likely, death. I doubted there were many bank robberies in Cuba. Security everywhere made sure it stayed that way and lurid soap operas emphasised the point, just in case you weren't convinced.

The same armed guards arrived at the busier, usually tourist orientated, shops every day to take away the profits. It was routine, only a lunatic would consider trying to rob them, but they remained alert, scanning the street and diverting pedestrians. Where did they take the money? The Treasury? A special government bank account? To Fidel? Did he sit at home counting the takings and planning fresh revolutions in South America?

The soap operas, while clearly low on production values, had grittily realistic story lines, often of petty crime, but quite graphic in their portrayal of small-time violence. Stabbings, muggings and burglaries were shown in all their nasty, explicit detail with no romanticising of the criminal whatsoever. They never got away with anything. Heroic, dedicated police officers delivered justice every time. The guilty were often shown sobbing at their fate (a very long sentence) and the message was clear: Don't do it. If you do we will catch you. And you won't like it. You have been warned.

We visited her oldest brother in Santa Cruz de Sur. Arriving again after nightfall I saw people on their verandas and patios, swishing at the air around them with voluminous white sheets. I soon found out why – thousands, millions of pinhead-sized biting black insects. I'd adapted to mosquitoes, which weren't really a problem, but these tiny horrors were too much. They drove me to distraction.

I covered up during the day, preferring sweaty heat to the constant onslaught of the insects – I can't remember what they were called. Yamilia's brother, Yordanis, who was a fisherman, said they were assaulted by them all day at sea. He shrugged a smiley, you just get used to it, shrug that made me feel very soft. Yordanis and his wife, Alicia, gave us their bedroom, their bed and their mosquito net, but the slightest gap or hole let in the pinheads, or maybe I imagined my skin crawling with them. Twice Alicia came to us, cleaned the bed and reset the net at Yamilia's request, due to my thrashing about. Not my proudest day.

We set off back the next day, Yordanis and family taking advantage of the car for a rare family reunion, eight of us squashed together; a blonde female hitch-hiker making nine later. When we stopped to stretch our legs Yamilia touched my arm:

'You have disillusion?' she said.

'No, no disillusion.'

Fifi drove, and uncomfortably, but uneventfully we made it to a checkpoint close to Lugareno where a curious guard finally flagged us down. We filed into his office and stood, while he examined all our documents. Yamilia, Fifi and Yordanis talked at once, explaining the overcrowded car. We were just a family returning home for a reunion. Sorry, but how else would we get home? The guard asked Fifi for his licence. Fifi patted his pockets, shook his head in exasperation at his stupidity – well, what an idiot, he'd gone and left it at home. The guard shook his head, beckoned me to him. He handed me my passport and licence. I understood him tell me to drive the rest of the way and something more that I didn't understand. In the car I asked Yamilia what he'd said,

'He say you have a very strange family,' she said, 'so many ages and different colours.'

They laughed about it the rest of the way. By the time we got home it was a completely different story, a few days later, unrecognisable.

Yamilia's father owned a smallholding he ran with his new wife. His house was of similar size and design to Yamilia's, very basic, but he had a fair piece of land where he grew fruit and vegetables and kept a few pigs, chickens and goats. He understood Yamilia's desire to leave the country, but said that, especially with money, we could be happy here. We have sun, sea, music, good land, rum, education and health he said. Nobody needs any more. He put his fingers to his lips, kissed them, then waved his hand at his land and the country and the sun.

The Elian story was running worldwide at this time. Elian had been washed up in Florida, his mother dead from the crossing and his father, separated, still in Cuba. The Miami Cubans had adopted him as a symbol of freedom and were determined to keep him from being returned to the clutches of Castro and the evils of communism. Fidel, after originally showing no interest, suddenly realised the political potential of the story and a tug of war developed between the land of the free and the boy being returned to his father in Cuba, which legally, the US was required to do. Castro used the story to whip the people into righteous indignation and patriotic fervour. Sally was full of the story, chanting Elian's name.

'Sally is very credulous,' said Yamilia.

Miami's Cuban community is ninety-five per cent white. Elian is white.

'If he had been black they would have thrown him back in the sea,' she said.

Elian was returned to his father after months of haggling.

My health improved despite the fiestas. Fresh food, clean air, water and sunshine had given me a healthy colour. I didn't flinch from photographs. But sleep was hard. I lay awake in the heat unable to settle. Villa Pan Americana had a constant breeze; there was none here. And it was noisy. In the country after dark a thousand creatures begin their nightly chorus of croaking and screeching. Dogs bark, confused cockerels crow all night. I got up and read, drinking a half bottle of rum, maybe more. I didn't get drunk, but slowly, after a few hours, my head began to nod and I finally slept at four or five in the morning, getting up way after the others around midday. Apart from some fuzziness I felt fine. Life was good and I had no problems, although this is probably where they began.

Then Rosa phoned. My visa had expired and I needed to leave the country to renew it. We'd both forgotten all about it. We drove home the next day.

If we publicly declare that Cuba is a threat to our security, forty million Mexicans will die laughing.
Mexican Ambassador

MEXICO

I spent two depressing nights in Mexico City. Disoriented and out of my element, I didn't venture far from the hotel, reading and just passing the time. At the airport I was advised to take a green taxi, any other colour and I could end up buried in the desert. The only incident of note came at breakfast on my first day when I had to convince a potential suitor that I wasn't gay. He finally left after twenty minutes, unconvinced.

I arrived back at the flat barely forty-eight hours after leaving, with a new visa. Yamilia was out and I didn't have a key. I phoned her cellular, but it was dead, probably out of credit. I found Rosa, who let me in. I asked her if she knew where Yamilia was.

'She hasn't been here,' she said.

'And you don't know where she is?'

'I don't know, Chris.'

Rosa cooked and ate with me. Yamilia and Rosa got on well on the surface, but now I sensed disapproval.

'She knows what time you come?' she said.

I nodded.

'She should be here.'

I was unsure if I wanted to pursue this. Rosa was happy to have us. It was in her interest for us to be together for the rent; she wouldn't risk that without good reason.

'Does she have somebody in Havana?'

'I don't know. It's your life, Chris. You can do better.'

I heard this often. I could do better: someone obedient and subservient; someone who was no trouble. I doubted Yamilia had survived for so long in Havana without help. Whoever helped didn't do it for nothing and they would still be around. But now she had the chance to break those ties. She wouldn't break them without being sure she wouldn't need to go back. If she even had that choice – she might be afraid to break with them. It could be dangerous for her. It could be dangerous for me.

'Let's see what she says,' I said.

She arrived while we were eating.

'Ay, sorry, mi amor. My phone empty and I have no money for taxi.'

I knew this wasn't true, although her face didn't betray it. She'd either spent the money I'd left her or she'd given it to someone. She joined us at the table and soon the atmosphere changed – a happy house. Yamilia could do that. She could do the opposite too.

We ate out that night.

'Where did you stay?' I said.

'In Havana with my friend. The one you meet. My *girl*friend. Stay Rosa's alone, I don't like.'

'You had Rosa or Lucia.'

'I'm not friends with Rosa. Lucia is busy.'

'The money I left you? You spent it?'

'We go out. Music, dancing.'

Her eyes slid to the side.

She was drunk when we got back to the flat. She took a jar of honey from the kitchen and poured it over her breasts, allowed it to trickle down her body, then lay on the low table, legs wide apart.

'Chris, lick it off,' she said.

I was tired and a bit pissed off. I hadn't enjoyed the food or her company, could still taste the diesel fumes of Mexico City and Havana.

'No,' I said.

I heard her shouting at herself, or me, as she showered. The bedroom door slammed against the back wall. She grabbed a few clothes, shouted some obscenities at me as she passed, and left. I didn't see her again for two days.

While she was away a distant cousin came to visit with her fiancé, a Cuban who didn't drink or smoke. He asked, very politely, for payment for some bootleg CDs that Yamilia had purchased on credit. I paid him and explained Yamilia's absence.

'Chris,' said her cousin, 'Yamilia is loco.'

That night I was with José. My cellular rang.

'What are you doing?'

'I'm with José in Old Havana.'

'No Yamilia?'

'She's gone.'

'Why?'

'It's a long story.'

'Will she be back?'

'I think so.'

'Hmm. I'm coming out in two weeks.'

'Splendid.'

'Do I need a hotel?'

'No. We've got a room for you.'

'We?'

'She'll be back by then.'

It is possible that a certain amount of brain damage has therapeutic value.
Dr Paul Hoch

SANTERIA

She returned full of smiles as though she had been away for five minutes. Yamilia and Lucia spent the morning shopping; they said had a surprise for me. With bags of provisions we took a taxi to a street of little houses, as close as they could safely stand to, what today, was an angry sea. We climbed some wooden steps, to be greeted at the top by a small black women dressed in white. She ignored Yamilia and Lucia, embraced me and whispered in my ear,

'You are about to have a taste of Afro-Caribbean religion.'

It must have been a practised phrase because Elisa had little English. What she did have was spoken beautifully, full of fun, music, eroticism and the tough as hell, mixed up history that is Cuba. Yamilia had decided on a 'blessing' because three bank transfers of $9000 for the possible purchase of the house had been confiscated by the USA and were sitting in the US Treasury. It later transpired that Paul had confiscated one of the transfers for himself.

Elisa may have been five feet tall, but it was a close-run thing. Attractive in a dizzy way, she was Yamilia's friend and a priestess of Santeria: worship of the saints, a religion so complex, with its brew of Spanish Catholicism and the beliefs of countless slaves who brought their own saints and stories from the villages of Africa, that I doubt if anyone fully understood it. Fortunately, like most things in Cuba, it didn't really matter. Elisa wore large, thick lensed glasses that added to her comical appearance. I was to be blessed in tandem with a Peruvian girl, travelling alone, whose problems, according to Yamilia, were of a serious nature.

'She's from Peru,' she whispered, as though this was one of her problems.

She certainly looked worried, wearing the brave smile of the about to be condemned. I suspected boyfriend trouble, but I didn't ask. Yamilia would tell me later.

Preparation for the ceremony took some time. It shouldn't have, but it did. By mid-afternoon everything was in place: live rooster, elaborate shrine, several large cigars, strategically placed candles, pieces of coconut shells, bottles of white rum, and an audience, always an audience. The audience grew, soon including Elisa's three teenage daughters (though she could pass for early twenties), Yamilia, Lucia and any number of neighbours who dropped by. They all needed to catch up on the gossip of the last twenty-four hours; discuss it, argue about it, forget about it and start all over again. I'd learned to accept the slow, haphazard pace of Cuban life, so I settled back with one of the bottles and watched the sea pounding the rocks with such force that the spray splattered my car, fifty yards from the beach. Havana was having a rough January. So much so that the Cubans behaved as the English would if temperatures dropped below freezing. They moaned about it.

Yamilia and Elisa decided that they were missing a mysterious, but essential ingredient and set off to a neighbour's house in search of it. They returned half an hour later in high spirits, empty-handed, but too stoned to remember what they'd gone for in the first place. Elisa decided that the Peruvian girl, Conchita, would have to wait until tomorrow, having divined that her problem was more serious than first thought. Conchita wrung her hands and got down to some serious worrying, although she didn't leave, and showed every intention of sticking around to see what happened to me. My situation was fairly simple: I was going to Panama and the US Embassy to politely request that the Treasury return my $27000. My UK bank had sent three transfers via the USA, all had been confiscated *en route* due to a law the new Bush administration had enacted, but neglected to tell anyone about, including my bank. Bluntly, they would confiscate any funds they suspected of being used for business purposes in Cuba, regardless of their origin. This ceremony was supposed to bring me good fortune for the trip and my quest.

Elisa's two-storey house was the last of a row along a rough road leading to a rocky beach on the outskirts of Villa Pan Americana. Wooden steps on the outside joined the two floors. A fair-sized living room was prepared for the ceremony. There were two small bedrooms, poky bathroom with shower, small patio and garden with a large wooden hut, and a balcony overlooking the sea. Her ambition was to go to the US to become a TV healer. She said she wanted a better life for her children. I had heard of tourists and writers paying $2000 for Santeria ceremonies. This had cost me the price of the provisions plus a few extra items for Elisa, no more than fifty dollars.

I'd been to a few of these ceremonies before and knew they got messy, so I wore old clothes. By the time they were ready I was relaxed and mellow. They would be spitting rum at me later, a terrible waste, so drinking as much of it as possible before they got going seemed like a good idea. I kept the cockerel company while they talked. I knew what was going to happen to it, and so did he judging by the look in his eyes. I picked him up and tried to calm him. I wasn't sure where his ear was, so I whispered where I thought it should be.

'Listen, I'm sorry about this. It wasn't my idea and I've always been kind to animals. This is just the way they do things here. You're an essential part of the ceremony, and, well, let's face it: you were going to end as dinner pretty soon anyway.'

He wasn't impressed.

I was asked to kneel in front of the shrine. Triangular and rising about six feet to its peak, it had shelves containing African ornaments and relics: wooden faces and big-breasted women. There were dozens of fruits, a couple of scrolls containing handwritten Spanish poetry, mirrors framed in copper and brass, some abstract and naïve Cuban paintings in blues and reds and yellows that looked decidedly erotic, although I wasn't sure why. The whole draped in muslin strips of blue; fresh flowers filled the spaces. Yamilia had raided my meagre possessions; a small basket contained passport-sized photos of me and a large pencil sketch drawn by a street artist in Havana. Small wooden and metal boxes lined the shelves, mostly containing dried flowers, though one had a mix of black and brown hair in it. I checked my head for missing locks, searching for connections between all this and my confiscated money.

Elisa asked me to speak to the shrine. I looked around the room, realising for the first time that I was the only man there. Women of varied age smiled back at me, nodding encouragement. I spoke to Yamilia.

'What shall I say?'

'Just speak, Chris. Speak what you want. Pray. You never pray before?'

I hadn't, and I didn't intend to start now. I studied the shrine and noticed new objects. A photo of Yamilia at the beach, smiling and sexy; wooden figures, male and female, entwined; a painting of two eyes, one black, one blue, melting into each other, and a new smaller eye of sea green emerging; an enormous wooden penis with a large pink mariposa impaled on its tip. I decided, with all eyes expectantly on me, to just go with the flow – again. I wanted to know what happened next. I spoke to the shrine, something like: 'Please can I have my $27000? I promise to use it well and not threaten the security of the USA. I promise not to incite Cuba into open warfare. I promise to uphold the American Way if you return my money, and I promise not to do it again. Something like that. I spoke quietly, in a low respectful tone. They didn't understand a word and seemed happy enough.

'What do you want, Chris?' said Elisa.

I mumbled something about wanting a safe trip. She picked up four pieces of coconut shell. They were roughly the same size and, if thrown, would land with the inside or outside curve facing upwards. She tossed the shells onto the floor. Three landed with the outside facing up, the other one down. This must have been good because it drew a murmur of approval. She repeated the process: all four up this time. Yamilia clapped her hands and smiled at me, eyes blazing with light. That light may have been contemplating some serious shopping, but I sensed something altogether more visceral. Was this some kind of fertility rite? Was this a blessing for a future child, or for my potency? That would explain why only women were here. Another man would change the atmosphere. José would have me out of there in seconds. But providing they didn't intend to sacrifice *me*, it could only be fun, I thought. Elisa threw the shells a few more times. The worst result was half and half; mostly three or four shells landed the right way up. She lit an enormous cigar, which suited her, took my hands in hers and puffed smoke at my chest, holding my eyes. She spoke at length in Spanish, a lovely melodic voice, so that I believed everything she said without understanding a word. Then Yamilia said,

'Now you must go down the stairs to the wood room. I don't come with you.'

I picked up the cockerel and a bottle of rum and followed the women down the stairs. The wooden hut was quite large, bigger than the room we'd just left. At the far end was a charcoal fire, with smoke rising and disappearing through a hole in the roof. Thick round candles lit the room. The walls were hung with coloured sheets, shades of red and pink and crimson, the floor laid with wooden boards that thumped as we walked. In the centre of the room was a low table with an enormous cake on it. It was tiered like a wedding cake, white and pink and studded with fruit: slices of peach, avocado, papaya, mango and melon. Elisa put a portable CD player on the floor and music filled the room, slow and heavy, accompanied by drums and violin. Above the charcoal fire sat an enormous pebble, a flat and smooth black rock really, speckled with white and sparkling silver. I let the cockerel go, took a swig of rum and put the bottle on the table. More bottles had appeared from somewhere. Lucia began to dance, lifting up her knees, one after the other, stomping on the boards, head back and eyes closed.

Elisa reached up and took my shoulders, guided me to where she wanted me to stand. I was light-headed, struggling to understand her. The hut was hot and smoky. It reminded me of the North American Indian sweat rites, where they fasted and spent days in a sweat tent, becoming pure again. They hallucinated, saw guiding spirits in birds and animals, and emerged cleansed with a clear path to their life. Something other than charcoal was burning, sweet and heady. Elisa was still talking at me. Conchita came to us.

'She wants you to stand here. Do not move. She says you may be more comfortable if you strip to your shorts. It will be very hot and messy here.'

It was the first time she'd spoken.

'So you speak English,' I said, stupidly.

She laughed and walked away, swigging from one of

the bottles. Elisa drew deeply on her cigar and blew more smoke at me, then took a mouthful of rum, stepped back, and with considerable skill sprayed it all over me. Lucia stopped dancing and did the same. So did Conchita. Then they all did. They circled me and sprayed me with rum until I was soaked. Stripping to my shorts was a good idea, particularly with the fire burning at the end of the room. They took great handfuls of the cake and began to cover me with it, rubbing it into my skin and hair. It was very, very hot. Conchita and a couple of others continued to rub the cake into my skin, like a lotion. Pieces of fruit stuck to me.

I grabbed what was left of a bottle. I felt happy and high. The air in the hut was intoxicating. The other women were dancing, not any recognisable moves, but trancelike stomping, arms waving and heads back. Lucia stripped to the waist, speaking a strange language, not Spanish – something else entirely; my upright, respectable nurse was expelling her demons. She affected Conchita, who laughed and began to concentrate on my pelvic area with the cake. Next time I looked Lucia was naked and staring at me with a fearful look in her eyes, a look I remember from old horror films where an 'evil' woman's eyes and mouth are exaggerated into an all-seeing expression that terrifies everybody. Conchita joined her. Lucia spoke to Conchita, watching me the whole time. Then Conchita spoke to me.

'Elisa is going to kill the bird. The blood will drip on the stone. You must mix your seed with it.'

'My seed?'

She looked down at my shorts.

'Yes, your seed.'

They were making this up as they went along. Freud said the Irish are impervious to psychoanalysis. I assume he never visited Cuba.

'How?'

Elisa had the cockerel in her arms. She shouted something to Lucia. Lucia shouted at me.

'Chris. Sexo. Like this.'

She made what would anywhere else have been judged an insulting gesture. She would have been calling me a wanker. She took my shoulders and stood me above the stone. I could smell our sweat mixed with everything else. Conchita knelt in front of the stone. Elisa, on the other side still held the now struggling cockerel. I'd been semi-aroused for a while, now, as I looked down, I'd become quite keen. Lucia continued to gesture, slapping my backside to instil urgency. There was no way. Absolutely no way. I was not going to toss myself off in front of twelve unhinged women, no matter how good I felt. Lucia shouted at Conchita. She still thought that I didn't understand, that all I needed was translation. Conchita said:

'Chris, you must…'

'No,' I shouted, 'you do it.'

So she did. It took about ten seconds.

They rubbed their hands all over me. The fire had been put out. Maybe the stone would have cracked with any more heat. I felt what Conchita was doing and watched as Elisa twisted the head off the cockerel in one swift movement. She held the dripping neck over the stone. Streaks of thin blood ran, hissing over the smooth surface. The white joined the red, like blood running through the white of an egg. The mixture rolled around the hot stone like little balls of mercury. I heard the sea crashing on the rocks and a brief hiss as the small white drops evaporated to thin lines, criss-crossed with blood. Conchita was breathing heavily. I'd stopped breathing altogether. Elisa pushed us aside and knelt in front of the stone. She stared intently at it as the heat of the stone swallowed the stains and they vanished. She stood and spoke to one of her daughters,

'Get Yamilia,' she said.

Yamilia stared at Lucia, naked and out of breath and burst into laughter. Conchita, also naked, and still kneeling at my side, turned crimson when Yamilia looked at her. I pulled up my shorts and waited to see what would happen next, although there was an air of finality to the proceedings. Elisa killed the music, Lucia and Conchita grabbed their clothes. Yamilia took the bottle from me and took a long pull from it. Then Elisa took her aside and they talked. Elisa spoke softly so I couldn't hear, gesticulating and occasionally pointing or nodding at me. Yamilia listened intently, asked a few questions and also looked over at me, serious and thoughtful. I felt like a piece of livestock.

Yamilia joined me in the shower and slowly, carefully washed off the rum and the contents of the cake. Smiling, she aroused me, stopping and starting, prolonging. Then, when she was ready, she took me inside her from behind, rushing to lie on the bed when I'd finished.

'Elisa say it is best for us this way,' she said.

For a while she behaved as though she was pregnant. It may have been wishful thinking or to justify the pot belly she was developing. She also referred obliquely to marriage and showed concern about my smoking and drinking; they might affect my potency. A visit to Raul showed nothing, but now she brought the subject up regularly when we were on good terms. I was ambivalent. I liked the *idea*, but a conversation with Yamilia from the year before came back to me. We were at her mother's house, surrounded by kids.

'Do you like children?' I said.

'Si,' she said, 'for five minutes.'

There are no great men, buster. There's only men.
Elaine Stewart: The Bad and the Beautiful

ANDY

I arranged to meet José in the early afternoon, but needed some cash. I also needed some clothes, so I drove to the Habana Libre, a few miles along the malecon. The Habana Libre, previously the Havana Hilton, was built by Meyer Lansky and the mafia before the revolution, keeping the then US backed dictator, Fulgencio Batista, sweet with monthly payments in excess of a million dollars. An impressive, if slightly dated structure, it could, if you didn't notice the people, feel like Vegas rather than Havana.

There was a queue for cash. A middle-aged man, not a Cuban, stood behind me in the line. He hovered closely, obviously keen to talk. I kept my back to him, although I could see his reflection in an opposite window. Despite the heat he was wearing jeans and a leather jacket, his long dark hair combed back and behind the ears. He moved past me in the queue and joined two girls, taking care to show that he wasn't pushing in, standing off to one side. He was easy with the girls, good Spanish and never lost for words or put off in any way. They were cautiously interested, though not enough for him, so he reclaimed his place in the queue. He wore a self-satisfied smile, carrying himself with confidence, completely at home. I avoided eye contact, was hung over and didn't want to talk

'So where do you take your women?' he said.

He was American. And this was a challenge more than a question. Getting right to it without embarrassment. I played the tourist.

'I had a women in my hotel,' I said, 'but I had to pay the staff. Turned out expensive.'

'That's no good. Get your own place. Have as many as you like and don't pay them so much. How much did you pay?'

I halved the price a tourist would be expected to pay. He didn't believe me, but made a show of considering it.

'That's not bad,' he said. 'How long are you here for?'

'I'm leaving in a couple of days.'

'England?'

'Yes.'

He nodded, not believing me again. The queue was slow, I felt obligated to say more – he was too close to ignore. I asked him without interest if he lived in Cuba.

'I rent a place here. Two months here, a month back home, saves problems with visas. I buy stuff and ship it back to the states.'

His dark brown eyes appraised me constantly. Smiling, although the smile never reached his eyes. Cool, unruffled, at home anywhere. He offered his hand.

'Andy.'

'Chris.'

I got my cash and my chance to leave.

'Nice meeting you,' I said, as he waited for his money.

'Sure,' he said, 'see you around.'

I parked in Old Havana, browsed among the book stalls in the Plaza Armas. Nearby was a shop that sold old books, memorabilia, bits and pieces: old film stills – Bogart, Laurel and Hardy, W C Fields, and rare books, photographs and documents. I dithered constantly over whether to buy anything. I love anything to do with old movies.

'They're second issues, don't bother.'

He must have grabbed his money and come straight after me. He picked up a still from *The Maltese Falcon*, showed me a number on the back.

'See this, stroke two, it's a second issue.'

I nodded, interested despite myself.

'Even if you just want it for framing they'll charge too much in here. This is for tourists.'

The implication was that I wasn't a tourist. Neither was he. We were in this together. 'Everything here is over-priced. Everything in this area is overpriced.'

I knew that. Overpriced for Cuba maybe, but still cheap. I wasn't interested in getting the best price everywhere, screwing the Cubans for every peso. I didn't say that though. I didn't say anything. I was still a bit disturbed that he'd turned up here, didn't like him any more for the information. I wanted to be away from his company, a strong, urgent feeling. I was also curious.

'Let's go get a drink,' he said, 'what do you drink here?'

'Silver Dry, mojitos sometimes.'

'Let's go.'

I chose the bar overlooking the harbour, where I was due to meet José in an hour, then immediately regretted it. He could find me there. I ordered a large rum and he had a beer. I wish I liked beer; it would have saved me a lot of trouble later.

'So you're on holiday here?' he said.

'I've been a few times.'

'Where are you staying?'

'The Sevilla,' I lied.

'That's a dump. You should rent a house. It's cheaper and you can do what you like. This whole area's a tourist trap.'

'Not all of it is. You don't have to walk far to find something different. I like it here.'

'Right. You got a woman here?'

'No.'

'Wise man. Fuck them all, hey?'

I looked out over the harbour, took a sip of my rum and didn't reply.

'You find they do everything? Fucked if I can get a decent blow job. You fuck them in the ass? You find they do that here?'

'Do you?'

'Pay them enough they'll do anything,' he said, contradicting himself.

He was baiting me, which gave me an excuse to be rude.

'Nothing to do with you.'

He spread his hands and smiled.

'Hey, no problem. Just curious.'

He lived out by the Habana Libre. Travelling back and forth via Mexico, two months in Cuba, one in the USA. Cuba was full of valuable antiques. Even the poorest homes had something, something they'd hung on to through necessity that had become valuable – furniture, paintings, books and magazines – everything, including film stills. He bought small stuff that was easy to ship, not big time, just enough to maintain his lifestyle.

'Cubans are fucking children,' he said. 'You have to deal with them like that. I looked over a house the other day, it was full of shit. But they had a few first editions and a signed photograph of Hemingway. They asked me a stupid fucking price for the whole houseful, shit furniture, everything. I knocked them right down. They squeal and shout like kids and I said "take it or leave it". They took it. I picked up the books and the photo. They shout "Hey, what about all this stuff?" I said "you can fucking dump it, I don't want it" and I walked out. Cunts. You have to be like that with them. The niggers are worse. So, you want to live here?'

'Maybe.'

'Fidel is a fraud,' he said, 'this whole revolution is a sham. And Raul? Just a drug dealer, helping the Columbians, even the fucking Russians now, offshore, to get drugs through the country.'

'You sure about that?'

'Fuck, you don't believe in any of this shit, do you?'

'I keep an open mind.'

'Then open it a bit further, my friend.'

You are not my friend.

José arrived. He saw Andy and raised his eyebrows at me. I gave him a slight shake of the head and hoped he understood. Andy just smiled. José was curious, pleased to meet somebody new, everybody was a potential opportunity.

'This is José,' I said, 'he's black.'

Andy laughed. José didn't understand, but he laughed anyway.

'José, this is Andy.'

Andy eased into fluent Spanish. I sat back and watched them talk. José spoke slowly enough for me to understand. Andy's Spanish was clear. They didn't talk about me and I didn't give them the opportunity by leaving the table. Andy bought us both a drink, drained his beer and said:

'OK. Business to be done. Good to meet you guys.'

He handed us both a card, shook hands and left.

The card contained his name, the Havana address and two phone numbers, one for Cuba and one for the USA. No business title.

'Nice guy,' said José.

'You think so?'

José didn't judge anybody on sight, except for the potential business value to him. I tore up the card and put the pieces in an ash tray. José shrugged and put the card in his wallet. I never saw Andy again. But José did.

'So, how is life with Yamilia?'

'She thought she was pregnant.'

'Is she?'

'No.'

He crossed himself.

'She wants to get married.'

'You going to *marry* her?'

'Maybe.'

'No. You can't do it. You are not a married man.'

We were silent for a while, watching the passing crowds.

'Look at those men,' said José.

'What?'

He pointed at the constant procession of couples passing, sometimes stopping and staring, sometimes finding a table. Middle-aged men with cameras, filming everything and seeing nothing.

'What am I looking at?' I said.

'Who do you think are the married men?'

'I don't care.'

'The men who dare not even *look* at the women here. Where do you think they would like to be?'

I said nothing.

'Not here, not with their wives' he said, 'but they are trapped. They are defeated. You want to be trapped with Yamilia?'

'That wouldn't happen to me.'

He laughed.

'They thought so too.'

'Why don't you like Yamilia?' I said.

'Really?'

'Really.'

'I told you. I think she is bad.'

'Why? Why is she bad? What do you know about her?'

'I think she is after your money. I think she is bad for you. She is crazy.'

'That's it? I know all that.'

'So you think she is after your money?'

'I think *you* are after my money, but we get along OK. Of course she likes my money. It can change her life. But we have fun. She knows me. She looks out for me. She

106

worries when I'm sick. We're happy most of the time. If it were just about money we'd be miserable. She's no worse than you. People don't like that she's a woman and sticks up for herself. You macho Cubans, you don't like it. She's a bit crazy, sure. Who isn't?'

He raised his eyebrows.

'A bit crazy?'

I ignored that.

'That's all you've got? That's why you don't like her?'

'She will bring you down,' he said.

I felt like getting drunk. I thought he had more to say. José was the inscrutable type, a diplomat. Most Cubans just come straight out with what they think, he didn't. And he didn't want to upset me. It was in his interests that I stayed happy.

'She won't bring me down,' I said.

'You love her too much.'

He had a point.

'The times before you came. I saw her with many men.'

'How many?'

He shrugged.

'Six. Maybe.'

So, probably three or four. Yamilia could pick and choose.

'Is that so bad? In a year?'

'That's only the ones I saw.'

I shrugged. Girl has to eat. I didn't expect her to sit at home while she wondered if I'd ever make it back.

'None of that bothers me, José. You sure it's not because she doesn't like you? Keeping you away?'

'No. I don't like that. It's not what I know. It's what

I feel. I have a bad feeling about her. She will stop you succeeding here.'

That was different. A bad feeling. I'd woken up with a bad feeling too.

'OK. This is what I think,' I said. 'Yamilia came to Havana when she was fifteen. Ten years ago. Hard for a woman to survive here for that long.'

'She came the same time as me. She slept in parks to begin with, like me. After two years I had a house and brought my whole family here.'

He tilted his chin at me – I was too soft to understand.

'Not easy,' I said.

'Not easy.'

'So she would need help.'

'For sure.'

'Do you think someone was pimping her?'

'No. She is too independent. But she would need help, protection.'

'Do you know where she lives?'

'No. Do you?'

'I think I know where she used to stay, maybe still does when I'm away.'

'Where?'

I told him about Magic Night.

'I think she got food and lodging at Lazaro's,' I said. 'I think she lived her own life, but paid her way with them. Maybe when she went to France she escaped from that, but now she's back. She deferred to Lazaro. I didn't like him. She ignored Amado and he ignored her. You think he is her boyfriend?'

'Maybe before. Now? I don't know. What is Amado like?'

'Your age. Arrogant, white, greasy, rude, probably stupid. Lazaro isn't stupid, dangerous maybe.'

'You could be correct. Maybe she wants to leave them. Maybe she is working with them. But while you are in Havana they will not leave her alone. Or you. They think they can get rich from you.'

José told me that one of his friends had been stabbed to death a few nights before.

'Why?'

He shrugged.

'No good reason.'

He seemed unconcerned. 'Friend' was a very loose term here.

'José,' I said, 'if tourism wasn't so important, if there weren't so many police and the penalties so strong – would the people, you know, the people around here – would they kill me?'

'Sure,' he said, before catching himself far too late. Then he shrugged unconvincingly, 'maybe, probably not.'

'I want to get away for a few days.'

'With her?'

'No.'

'Come to Santiago with me and my girlfriend. I have a good business for you there.'

'I'll think about it.'

After much pleading from José I left him with my car. He loved driving despite having no licence. He loved showing off too. I took a taxi home.

Yamilia and Lucia were drinking beer when I got back. A film was on TV, apparently ignored. It was late.

'Long time at bank,' she said.

I ignored her, went through to the kitchen and poured a tumbler of rum. When I sat down they were both staring at me. Lucia was nervous, not sure if she should stay.

'Many people in bank, Chris? In Cuba bank is very slow, but Chris, they stay open for you? All this time? Is dark now. You very special person.'

She turned to Lucia for appreciation of her joke. Lucia didn't understand, but she knew what was happening. She stood up and kissed Yamilia, came to me and we kissed cheeks.

'Ay, Chris,' she said, waving her hand at the fumes.

As Lucia reached the door Yamilia said,

'Borracho.' Drunk.

'Ciao, manana,' said Lucia as she closed the door.

'Where you go?'

'To the bank. Then I saw José.'

'Ah, José,' she said, as though this explained everything. 'Your good friend, the knife man. You have good time? Fiesta? He find you woman?'

'Just talk.'

She shook her head. José meant women and trouble.

'Where did you stay when I was in Mexico.'

'Ah, so José make trouble for me and now you come to the house drunk. I tell you, I stay with my friend.'

'You stay with Lazaro, with Amado.'

She folded her arms and said nothing.

'You don't tell me the truth.'

'The truth, verdad?' she spat the word. 'You go to José and speak me of truth? Believe what you like.'

'You just want to steal from me.'

She flew at me and tried to slap my face. I caught her arm and pushed her away.

'Fuck off,' I said.

'Fuck off? You want me fuck off?'

She packed a bag in two minutes.

'You fuck off,' she said as she slammed the door.

It was soon late enough to call Paul.

'We have a logo,' he said. 'We're a registered company, Eternity Travel. I'm looking at advertising and we're nearly there with the ABTA.'

I told him about Andy.

'He sounds useful. Are you seeing him again?'

'No, I didn't like him. And Yamilia's gone.'

'Again?' He wasn't interested. 'She'll be back.'

The only reliable 24-hour bar in Villa Pan Americana is in the hotel. The sole customer on a quiet Monday night, now Tuesday morning, I knew I was keeping the barman from his sleep, so I tipped well with every drink. The enormous lobby, a mass of chairs, tables, fountains and pool tables could be lively, but tonight was funereal. I had played pool with Yamilia here. I wasn't tired and drank one rum after another. The barman informed me sadly that he wasn't allowed to play pool on duty. I spotted a woman serving at reception about seventy metres away, wandered over, pulled up a stool and chatted to her. Bored and pretty in the tight blue uniform of the hotel, she wore white shirt, knee length skirt, high heels and a tiny jacket. Maria spoke good clear English, one of the recently trained for the tourist industry. I wanted to nuzzle her large breasts, eat her and lose myself in her. I was in love. I wanted to marry her.

I made regular treks back to the bar for more rum. She was happy to talk and relieve the boredom. There were few guests and nothing for her to do, though she kept a wary eye open for the CDR. I told her I'd finished with my woman. She gauged my age and worth. I told her she was very beautiful. She smiled.

'What is your girl's name?'

'Yamilia.'

'A nice name,' she said.

'Yes.'

Is she a nice girl?'

'No.'

She raised her eyebrows.

'I like bad women.'

'That is very stupid.'

I wondered if it would be possible to fuck her. Of course not, she'd lose her job. Later, another time, another place, maybe, but that would bring conditions. I didn't love her that much.

'I need a woman.'

'You want a woman, *now?*'

'Yes.'

It was 3.00; Villa Pan Americana was fairly conservative and respectable for Cuba. It was fast asleep.

'You will not find a woman here, it is too late. You must go to Havana, but at this time it is dangerous for you.'

'Can you call me a taxi?'

'Of course, but are you sure?'

I gave her a look intended to convey that unless *she* had

an hour to spare, yes, I wanted a taxi. Whatever my look actually conveyed – drunken idiot, probably – she just smiled and lifted the phone. The taxi arrived immediately; it was just round the corner. I knew that. I could have walked. As I made my way to the door she called out:

'Where will you go?'

'Habana Vieja.'

'Be careful.'

'The Ambos Mundos.'

'It is your hotel?' said my driver.

'No, I want a woman.'

'I can find you a woman.'

'No, thanks. I'll find one.'

I woke the staff in the Ambos Mundos, had another drink and walked to Cathedral Square. It was deserted and silent, though when I stopped at its centre I could hear the whirring of fans, snoring and the fluttering of caged birds. A black jagged shadow pointed at me from the cathedral, a full moon behind it. A cat padded indifferently past. The square seemed larger with the café tables cleared away. I felt safe standing there, unsure which way to go.

I chose O'Reilly, the narrow street that ran parallel to Obispo, but without its bars and the light that went with them. The only light here was from the moon, made weak in the street by the tall buildings, but it was lovely, silvery and peaceful – in tune with the silence. The lights of the Sevilla hotel a half-mile away at the top of the street guided me as I walked past the alleys and side streets without turning my head. I had no sense of danger, a blind faith in my safety. As I approached the Sevilla a door opened, a girl beckoned me inside and quickly closed the door. We stood at the foot of a narrow staircase. She fired rapid Spanish at me. I didn't understand, but nodded anyway. What else could she be offering? What else could I want? She wore a short skirt, light make up, her long black hair was shiny and combed. I followed her up four long flights. Had she known I was coming? Her balcony overlooked the street. Did she sit there all night waiting for a drunk, lost soul to drift by? Had Maria phoned her just in case I happened to pass?

On her balcony I gazed out over the rooftops. She stood beside me, spoke and beckoned me inside. This was not a social call; she was a practical woman. She said it would be fifty dollars. I looked at her long legs, her severe pretty face and straight black hair. I said that would be fine.

An hour later, to the minute, she asked for her money and invited me to leave. I hadn't finished, suggested some possible solutions and counted out another fifty. She sighed, shrugged huffily and knelt back on the bed. Later, as the night's frustration finally left me, I watched the full moon through the window and threw back my head and laughed. It came from deep down; I was laughing at myself, the moon, the world and all its silly business, not her. But she didn't like that. Not at all. She spewed a stream of invective at me, none of which I understood, although the tone hinted at her desire for me to be out of her house, quickly. Way down the street I realised I hadn't got my watch. My watch: my insurance, my lifesaver. I turned round, mildly panicked and walked back. I had no idea which house I'd been in until I heard a voice from above. She stood on her fourth floor balcony, watch in hand, shouting to attract my attention. She tossed the watch in my direction. I got a palm under it before it bounced out and landed on the pavement. I put it on and checked it. It was fine. As I thanked her she yelled a parting salute. Whatever she said, it wasn't 'Take care', or 'Come back soon'. She either had no idea what the watch was or she was just honest. Probably honest. Most Cubans are, no matter what you might have read.

The barman washed glasses as I returned to the hotel. He smiled and shook his head as I approached. I carried my drink to reception. It was nearly seven, when Maria would finish her twelve-hour shift.

'So, did you find a woman?'

I nodded.

'Are you happy now?'

'Si.'

She smiled. Did she know? She didn't ask where I'd been.

'Go home, Chris. Go home and sleep.'

She was right. I had nowhere else to go. I didn't look at the empty flat as I made my way to bed. A coma awaited, I could sleep all day. An hour later somebody woke me. It was Yamilia. She lifted the sheet and climbed into bed. As she was snuggling up to me she suddenly jumped as though an electric current had passed through her, and leapt out again.

'You stink of fucked woman. She piss on you?'

She grabbed her clothes and stomped out. I heard the front door slam.

The smell of cooking woke me. My stomach churned

as I sat on the bed. I didn't eat the previous day. In the bathroom mirror my face had lost its colour, my hair a tangled mess. More nightmares. I waited for the shower to run cold and stood under it for a long time. Only then did I manage to get a toothbrush in my mouth without throwing up. Coffee, bread, water and fruit were on the living room table. In the kitchen Yamilia was serving ham, eggs and potatoes. She stopped and stared at me for a long moment, one hand on hip.

'Is no important,' she said, then looking down at the plate, 'grease,' she pronounced it "gress", 'is good for your stomach when you drink too much.'

She nibbled bread as I ate. She wore a pair of my shorts and one of my t-shirts, her hair tied back. She looked older, serious. She slipped on her sandals and walked to the door, stopped to answer the ringing phone.

'Is your friend, the knife man.'

It wasn't, not directly, it was the police.

'Come and collect your car. And your friend, collect him too.'

José was at a Havana police station. He'd been stopped late at night, no doubt showing off in front of his friends. Another fine. I said I'd get him in a couple of hours.

'You give your car to José?'

I nodded. She stared for several seconds, an expression of studied patience.

'You stay here?' she said.

'Si. You coming back?' I said.

She smiled.

'Later.'

I paid our fines and brought José to the house. We collected Celia, his new girlfriend, on the way. Rosa was cleaning the flat. Celia was slim with a long serious face and big, mournful eyes. She solved the problem of curly, wiry hair by cropping it close to her scalp. She wore masculine, wide, round-toed black shoes with short skirts, an unusual combination even for Cuba. Quiet, tending to watch and listen, her English was better than José's, though she didn't make a show of it. Her voice was deep, amused, knowing and possibly naughty, like she'd been smoking from the age of ten. José treated her like an accessory, rarely acknowledging or speaking to her.

I asked José about the trip to Santiago. They had booked the train for the journey in three days time.

'Will you come?'

'I don't know, maybe. Yamilia is not here.'

'Why?'

Rosa shouted from the kitchen.

'What did she say?'

'She said you should find a new woman,' he said.

Celia was uncomfortable. After a few minutes she went into the kitchen to talk to Rosa. Not long afterwards she was helping with the cleaning.

'What about the business?' I said.

'We know some people. They want to rent cars to tourists. They need someone to buy the cars.'

'What do I get?'

'They rent the cars. You get half the money.'

'How much?'

'I don't know. How many cars you buy? Come with us and talk with them.'

'I'll join you later. I have some things I want to do. I'll drive; tell me where you'll be.'

He handed me a card with the name of a hotel on it. 'They will pay', he said, and winked at me.

'Have you not remarked,' said Candide, 'that yonder young peasant girl is a very pretty brunette?'

'She has something very taking in her countenance,' said Cacambo.

Candide

TRINIDAD

I drove slowly, taking my time, thinking. I reached Trinidad as the sun was setting. Near the south coast of central Cuba, and a beautiful Unesco World Heritage site, Trinidad is also a tourist trap and, not in the mood for all that, I found a casa particular, a private house. The sights could wait for another visit. They always do. I rented a tiny room with a balcony overlooking a narrow cobblestone street.

I bought a couple of Cuban sandwiches, a bottle of rum and sat on my balcony, my diary open, as the sun sank below the pastel-coloured houses. My cellular was with José, blocked for foreign calls. Yamilia called regularly; when she heard his voice she would hang up. Swept along by the flow of other people's wants and needs, I had no time to consider anything. I wanted some quiet, some thinking space. In a whirl of fast-spoken Spanish I often had little idea what was going on. Yamilia still held the strongest pull on my emotions, if not my reason. José felt like a friend, not the most sensible of friends and nowhere near my age like Raul or Tony, but still a friend. That was it. Or I could go it alone. I would never be short of women or offers of friendship, but that was a dangerous path to take. There weren't any safe paths.

The balcony next to mine erupted in a mass of movement, colour and female voices. Four women were in animated discussion about some clothes, deciding what to wear. A couple held masks to their faces, swapping and laughing; one noticed me, jumped theatrically in surprise and beamed a smile at me:

'Ay, buenos noches senor.'

The others turned and four curious faces studied me like a zoo exhibit. Beyond returning the greeting, my Spanish failed me, as it often did when meeting new people without the help of Yamilia or José. I offered the bottle. They passed it around, each taking a sip, probably out of politeness, until it was back with the woman who had noticed me. Instead of handing the bottle back, she climbed over to my balcony.

'American?'

'English.'

She nodded as though she approved.

'We can't drink now because we are performing tonight.'

'What are you performing?'

'Dancing and music. I am a dancer. Dancing, music, story and history. It's a mix.'

Her English was near perfect. In her late twenties, maybe more, with light skin, a pretty, open face, she had an easy smile that looked like it wanted to be there all the time.

'Your English is very good.'

'Thank you. How long are you in Cuba for?'

'I live here.'

This, rather than anything in particular about me, seemed to grab her interest.

'Where?'

'In Havana.'

'With a woman?'

'Before, yes. Not now.'

She responded to a shout behind her.

'I'm sorry. I must leave now.' She slapped a leaflet on the table. 'Come tonight. It will be fun. And there is a party afterwards.'

She climbed back to her balcony and disappeared with the others. I read the leaflet. Caliente: Hot. I could still hear the animated conversation next door. Caliente? So much for private contemplation.

The performance in a dusty, crumbling hall was chaotic, a typically Cuban mixture of high energy, colour, Santeria, love and earthy sex – it was great. Although overtly sexual it was never crude. About twenty people made up the group. Noemi was one of the backup dancers, supporting the main theme. Sometimes two performers held the stage, at other times the whole group. At the end they spilled from the stage. Noemi poked my shoulder as the bottom-wiggling, rumba-dancing troupe danced among the audience.

I expected the party to be private, but afterwards the whole group went to a nearby bar. Behind the bar were enormous grounds in what appeared to be the ruins of an old colonial property, with lone detached columns, archways and dried up fountains, mazelike in its size and strangeness. We sat away from the others, who had shown little interest in me or, as I hoped, assumed we'd paired off. All felt loose, free and fresh. I realised that this was the first occasion in a long time that I'd been away from what was a small group of people, that I rarely wandered or explored alone anymore.

Noemi and the group outdid the usual Cuban love of colour with some extravagant combinations. Noemi wore baggy orange linen pants, a bright green vest and a red headscarf over her tied back hair. Although small, she appeared strong and powerful, slim and athletic rather than worked out, a thin silver chain around her neck, bangles and coloured beads on her left wrist and a single ankle bracelet above red leather sandals. Her slightly boyish face had hints of Chinese around the eyes, cheekbones and mouth, heightened by a thoughtful nature although she laughed easily and often. She had bright, childlike eyes. There was nothing broken about her, no signs of disappointment with life. There was nothing broken about Yamilia, but she was defiant, always wary of deceit and betrayal. Noemi was easy with herself.

A full moon dominated a sky full of stars, still visible from most places in Cuba, not yet obscured by artificial light and pollution. Lizards darted around the pillars while other creatures rustled in the unkempt grounds. The night chorus found its voice. A cool breeze helped a general sense of well-being. I felt completely at ease, expecting nothing.

'Where did you learn English?'

'At university.'

'What did you study?'

'Law. I wanted to be a lawyer.'

'Like Fidel.'

She laughed.

'Yes, like Fidel, but he is also the reason I am not a lawyer. There is no reward for my skill, I prefer to dance. The money is better and this is a good life. I can be a lawyer when I'm forty.'

'Forty is too old to dance?'

'For me, I think it will be.'

She lit one of her own cigarettes and poured herself some rum.

'You live in Cuba? How long have you been here?'

'A few months.'

'And how long will you stay?'

'As long as I can.'

She nodded and smiled, to herself rather than me. I was being sized up, accurately and quickly. I felt a little naive in her company, as though she was holding something back. 'Why are you in Trinidad?'

'I'm on my way to Santiago. A friend has a business idea for me.'

'What business?'

'Are you CDR?'

'Of course, later I will have you arrested and put in jail.'

'Cars,' I said, 'for tourists to rent.'

'Your friend can do this?'

'I'll find out.'

'Be careful with that. It can go wrong.'

'How?'

'I don't want to spoil anything for you. Just be careful who you deal with and think about everything.'

She yawned and stretched her arms behind her. She wasn't wearing a bra and smiled when she caught me looking. She took my wrist and studied my watch for a few seconds. She nodded.

'Why do you stay at a casa particular?'

'I don't like hotels.'

She asked about Yamilia and I gave her a brief history. She seemed to form a picture without needing to pry, satisfied that she understood or knew all she needed to know, able to draw her own conclusions without too many questions.

'I needed some time to myself,' I said.

She laughed, shaking her head.

'And here you are.'

We sat on my balcony late into the morning. Trinidad, unlike Havana, was silent at this hour, only an urban fox, losing its brief stand-off with a screeching, arch-backed cat disturbed us. I wasn't drunk, felt clear-headed, but pleasantly tired, as though a rare dreamless sleep might await me. Noemi stretched extravagantly and yawned.

'It's very late, I'm so tired. If you want to fuck it will have to be now.'

'I'm tired too. Let's sleep.'

I woke late the next day. The troupe was long gone. A Caliente leaflet lay on the bedside table. On the back she'd written: "We will be in Havana next month for one week. Find me if you want to. You snore!"

From Trinidad I drove to Camaguey and checked into

a hotel where I'd stayed before with Yamilia. I ate in the hotel restaurant and returned to a new balcony above a busy street. Tonight there were no adjacent balconies or beautiful dancers to change my plans. I was happy to sip rum and people watch. I also had good memories of times spent here with Yamilia and didn't want to tarnish them.

I set off early the next day after another dreamless sleep. On an impulse I took the turning for Lugareno. An ugliness I hadn't noticed before surprised me. An enormous decrepit factory dominated the landscape with rusty overgrown rail tracks leading to the village for miles. Long redundant wagons and buildings littered the tracks which ran by the side of the road. It must have once provided a living for the inhabitants. Now it looked as though only those with funds from relatives in Miami were living much above subsistence level. Yamilia's family didn't have any relatives in Miami.

I toyed with the idea of talking to Yamilia's mother. I'm not sure why; she spoke no English and my Spanish wouldn't stretch to what I wanted to say. I drove down the dusty uneven street of small single-storey dwellings, each with a front porch and a bigger garden at the back, usually containing a pig or two and chickens. The luckier Miami funded houses had new coats of paint, patios and garden furniture – TVs, music systems and video players inside, others showed their age and lack of investment. All this I'd seen before, visited many of the neighbours. There was no sadness to it. People here didn't waste time regretting their lot; they just got on with it. I didn't see a superior attitude from the haves, although it was probably there. Houses stayed full of life, children and activity no matter what. If anything, the more prosperous became more subdued as they considered what they had, took on a certain pride in it and thought about what they wanted next. And the children everywhere were just that – children – they didn't notice. All this, naive no doubt, from a European with money in his pockets. But it's what I saw and felt.

The front porch was empty as I approached Yamilia's house. I'd already decided to keep going. I looked down the side of the house to the back garden. Yamilia's mother was hanging out some washing. She was laughing. The wind blew a white sheet horizontal on the line and I caught a glimpse of Yamilia, pegs in hand, laughing at the same joke before the sheet floated down, obscuring her again. I drove on and parked fifty yards down on the other side of the street, adjusted the side mirror to the scene. Yamilia still wore my shorts, her hair a long curly tangle. They were talking and laughing. I watched until they walked back into the kitchen, then I drove away.

Yamilia had been in Havana four days before. I knew that. Had she hitched down? That was by far the most common method of travel, but not for Yamilia if she had alternatives. Train or bus? Possibly. She could have flown to Camaguey. She'd do that if she had the money and it wouldn't have been hard to embezzle it from me; I wouldn't have noticed. It didn't matter. What was important was the thud of shock and longing that hit my chest when I saw her. The feeling that no matter what I got up to here, in business or otherwise, life was empty without her. I really believed I'd shaken it off, that I could control it. The tension in my stomach and the way I gripped the steering wheel told me I couldn't.

But I was glad she was here, glad she was away from Havana. I wanted to drive around the block, go back and see her; stay there with her and forget Santiago. Instead I stopped at the next store and bought a bottle of rum. I nursed it in my lap, sipping regularly as I drove. By the time I reached Santiago and found the hotel on the card José had given me, the bottle was empty.

There are three sexes; males, females and girls.
Ambrose Bierce

SANTIAGO

The hotel was a Vegas like structure, similar to the Habana
Libre, built by the mafia before the Americans were thrown
out. At the desk I showed my credit cards, the girl shook
her head, said everything was taken care of. I was impressed. José said they would pay for everything. I doubted
it. In Cuba *you* paid, they didn't. I began to wonder who
these people were.

Santiago is much hotter than Havana. It has a history
of being the starting place for much of Cuba's revolutionary
history. Any protest that still remained usually started
there. I knew José was proud of his origins. Santiago has
the top baseball team and he always supported them in
favour of the Havana team, Industriales. I took the lift to
my room.

The air-conditioning hit me. The room was big and
luxurious: two big beds, shower and large bathroom, writing table, built in wardrobe space, vanity mirror, wall-length
window opening on to a balcony with a great view of the
city. And three women. A tall blonde lay on the bed reading a magazine; a black girl leaned on the balcony admiring

the view. Another girl sat combing her long black hair in front of the mirror. She had light brown skin and a serious, studious face. Whoever sent them had been trying to cover all tastes. None of them looked over twenty-five; the girl at the mirror could have been a teenager.

I was tired, dirty and hot. The sight of them unaccountably depressed me and I felt even more tired. I thought though, that a reaction would be expected. I needed to be in control. 'Buenos dias,' I said, and threw my bag onto the bed.

I nodded to the blonde, then at the bag. She immediately began to unpack it and put things away. I took the hand of the girl at the table.

'I'm going to take a shower,' I said, as I closed the bathroom door. In the shower I asked the girl how old she was. She said nothing, just studied me with curious intensity. She washed me and let me guide her to what I wanted.

I wanted it to last about an hour. If I was cold and didn't think about what I was doing, or look at what I was doing, I thought I could maintain indifference, get it over with and get some sleep. An hour later I stood behind the blonde as she knelt on the bed, thinking and watching now, just wanting it to end; bored and very tired. The black girl had returned to the balcony. The young girl though, since the shower had just watched, watched every move, studied our faces. She tilted her head this way and that, like a conscientious student watching an experiment. I couldn't finish. If I hadn't cared about the impression I was making I'd have given up. She moved behind us and, sighing with impatience stuck her tongue into my arse. I pushed the blonde away and moved to lie on the bed, but she held me upright, leaving me standing while she lay on the bed, her head tilted back towards me. The other two watched with amused interest. Then, when I'd been sure I was done, nothing left, using her hands and mouth she made me come again. The instant I relaxed she righted herself, and, task completed, dressed in seconds.

All three stood by the door ready to leave. I fumbled with my jeans looking for some money. They stared, mildly offended. The young girl tossed her hair imperiously, gave me a curt nod and, ignoring them, left the room. The blonde said,

'No, that was Hello to you. Welcome to Santiago.'

She gave me a look; that look, as I stood there, middle-aged and naked with my crumpled jeans in my hands. They laughed, gave me a pleasant smile, and were gone.

I slept for twelve hours before meeting José and Celia the next day. We sat outside a bar in a large plaza. I felt refreshed and drained at the same time. Ready for anything and not too concerned about what happened. Even the feelings about Yamilia were muted.

'Here they come,' said José.

Four young men stood at the table, polite, waiting for introductions. Despite the heat they were well-dressed, smart jeans or trousers, shirts, a couple of nice linen jackets, expensive sunglasses and mobile phones. I wore shorts, flip-flops and a t-shirt. Celia wore shorts too, although José had dressed for the occasion. He was nervous, possibly in awe of the company, Celia relaxed and cool, a reversal of their Havana roles. I stood to shake hands. They seemed surprised by me, maybe my age or appearance. José would have told them about me – what he'd told them I didn't know.

The first three gave solid handshakes and neutral expressions. The fourth turned his back on me and sat down. He spoke angrily to the others, telling them to get on with it. They sat while he stared pointedly around the square, his sunglasses still in place, anywhere but at me. I looked at José and Celia. He behaved as though nothing had happened. Celia giggled.

'Leris can speak English,' said José.

Leris outlined their proposal. The silent one turned his sunglasses on me. For pride's sake I returned his stare, and then blanked him completely, as though I was dealing with three people. Celia kicked me beneath the table and winked. The proposal was simple. I would buy some cars, nearly new ex-rentals, and they would hire them out to tourists. Beyond supplying the money I wouldn't have to do anything and they would give me a share of the profits. José or Celia, who travelled regularly between Havana and Santiago, would bring the money every few weeks. I wondered what could go wrong and remembered Noemi's vague warning.

'What percentage do I get?'

'Sixty-forty in our favour,' said Leris.

'No,' I said, 'fifty-fifty.'

Leris showed no surprise. Silent man stood up, his metal chair tipped over and clattered on the cobbled surface as he shouted at his companions. I recognised obscenities from his tirade before he stomped away across the square. I looked round the table. The four men shrugged without embarrassment or concern; it seemed this surprised nobody but me. Celia giggled and kicked me again.

Leris made a call and spoke rapidly in Spanish, followed by a yes or a no to some questions.

'How many cars will you buy?'

'Three.'

'Will you buy more if it goes well?'

'Yes.'

'Si,' he said into his phone, then nodded.

'OK,' he said and cut the phone.

José ordered a bottle of rum. We poured and touched glasses. I didn't want to see the cars, I left that to José. I said I'd give José the money in a week or so. We talked for a while, but they were keen to leave.

When they were gone we sat in silence for a while, draining our glasses, and then headed for another bar. As we walked Celia took my arm, linking it with hers. She looked up at me often, rubbing her shoulder against me; sometimes our thighs would touch as we walked. At first I thought she was strange, even ugly, but she wasn't, just different. Her eyes were warm, her smile open and inviting. José walked behind or in front, greeting other people and taking little notice.

As we poured from a new bottle they seemed on the verge of laughter.

'How were the women?' said Celia.

'Three women,' I said, 'very generous.'

Celia clapped her hands together, laughed and curled up in her chair, showing her pants and not caring in the least. I looked from one to the other. José drew a breath and blurted:

'They only mean to send two.'

'What?'

'They only send two women.'

'Chris,' said Celia, 'they only send you two women. What do you think about that?'

She drew out her vowel sounds like a Hollywood Mexican. She was a different character, as though Havana intimidated her, frightened her into a shell; here she was flirty, mocking and confident. She laughed her dirty laugh, enjoying my confusion. I turned to José,

'What's going on?'

'These people, they are from the university. They have plans for the money. When I heard their idea I told them about you. They asked if you would do it. They were very interested so I arranged this meeting.'

'And?'

'They wanted you to say yes. They asked if you liked women.'

Celia burst into laughter again.

'And do you, Chris? Do you like women?'

'I told them that you did,' said José. 'The next time they brought two women with them. They said they would send them to your room.'

'And?'

'It is not only the people you saw today. There are more. And a girl who is also from the university. When I told them about you she was very interested.'

'Why?'

'I told them about the money you gave to the ballet. That money. It is like a million dollars here.'

'Chris is a *good* man,' said Celia.

'But this is business,' I said.

'No. Well yes, it is business, but they want the money for other reasons.'

'So what has the girl got to do with it?'

'I told you. She was interested. She said she would go to your room with the two other women. They didn't like it, especially Arturo, but she does what she likes.'

'Arturo?'

'You fucked his girlfriend, Chris,' said Celia, 'he came to look at you today. You think you will be friends?'

'She is very serious,' said Jose.' 'She believes in Fidel. She is going to be a doctor, go to Africa and work for nothing. When she heard about you she asked many questions. She was very interested.'

'Imagine all the people, living life in peace,' sang Celia. She stuck out her tongue when I glared at her.

'What's her name?'

'Isabel,' said Celia. 'Beautiful Isabel.'

'How old is she?'

'Eighteen,' said Jose.

'Jesus.'

'Chris, she is a woman,' said Celia. 'She want to meet good man. She want to learn from good man. What you teach her, Chris? You teach her how to be good?'

'She is the daughter of a security officer,' said José. 'She is very serious about her education.'

'What kind of security officer? How high?'

He shrugged. Celia lifted her hand above her head.

'This high, Chris.'

'Fuck, Jose. That could have been dangerous. Why didn't you tell me?'

'I didn't know she would come. Anyway, she's not stupid.'

'He find out, he will cut off your pinga,' said Celia. 'What did she do, Chris? What did she teach you?'

'She competed with the two others,' I said.

'That's good for you. So you have a good time!' she said. 'What did she do?'

'I'm not telling you.'

'No problem. She will tell me.'

'She didn't say anything to me,' I said.

'She won't speak English,' said José.

'I can speak some Spanish.'

'Not enough for her.'

'Why won't she speak English?'

'I told you. She is serious. Fidel has not spoken English for many years. Because of the Americans. She is the same. She is very smart. Leris had to speak to her before he could accept fifty-fifty.'

The phone call, of course. And the women in the hotel. You just couldn't do that here without influence. I wondered what they wanted the money for.

'What did you *do* to her, Chris?' said Celia.

That night, alone in my room, there was a tap on the door. It was Isabel. I wondered how she managed to get in. Then I remembered her father. I stood stupidly as she walked past me into the room. She wore glasses, serious and studious as ever, like a schoolgirl. She picked up the book I'd been reading. English language books are hard to find in Cuba. The shops stock mainly political tracts in favour of Cuba. The markets have some discarded tourist books, but even there I hadn't found much. I read anything in English. At night I preferred novels, but tonight I had only an account of the clandestine war waged on Cuba by the United States. The numerous attempts on Fidel's life; the poison in his beard; the capsules in his milkshake. Ridiculous, but true. The bombs in the clubs; the air raid on Havana; the Olympic athletes blown out of the sky. None of it reported in the western media.

She studied the book, glancing curiously at me. I said something to her in Spanish. She glanced at me again briefly, but didn't respond. She put the book down and began an inspection of my clothes in the wardrobe. She studied the labels. She found my passport, looked through the stamps from other countries, studied the photograph, spent a long time looking at the Cuban medical stamps giving me permission to stay for treatment. She took the credit cards from my wallet and leafed through my address book. Then she found my diary. I wasn't concerned. She wasn't snooping. She was looking at another life. Taking it in. She'd chosen her path already. I envied her. I wished I could be doing what she was doing, wished I believed what she believed. She read slowly, every page, every word. She went out to the balcony. I stood next to her. We could see the lights of the city and the sea beyond it.

'Bonito,' I said.

No response.

'Smile,' I said.

She smiled. Then she pulled at the neck of my t-shirt, studied the scar on my shoulder, seemed to resolve something in her mind.

She stayed with me. We didn't do anything. I woke in

the night with her arm draped across my chest. She looked utterly at peace. I lay awake for hours. Then, when it was light, I woke myself with my snoring. I shuddered and looked around, wiped some saliva from my chin. She sat at the table, my diary in front of her, watching me in the mirror. She came to the bedside, kissed me on the forehead and stared for what seemed like an age. Then she said:

'Smile.'

Later that day we travelled back to Havana together. José slept across the rear seats. Celia sat in the front with me, legs apart, adjusting the air-conditioning so it would blow up her dress. She fiddled with a CD, finished and sat back, passed me the bottle of rum, lit a cigarette for me. The music was some Cuban stuff about love and loss and sex and life. She sang along.

'Chris. Tell me. What did you do with Isabel?'

'Nothing.'

'OK,' she said.

Ten minutes later she leaned over and put her face in my lap. I pulled her up, turned her face towards me:

'What are you doing?' I said.

She looked, not entirely kindly, at José on the backseat.

'I know him. He won't wake up for hours.'

And she went back to what she was doing.

Tisn't beauty, so to speak, nor good talk necessarily. It's just it. Some women'll stay in a man's memory if they once walked down the street.
Rudyard Kipling

Dancing

I dropped José and Celia in Havana. Celia put an arm around a sleepy José's waist and nuzzled his neck as they walked to his flat. As I started the car they both turned, José gave a small wave, Celia winked and turned quickly away.

I heard female voices and laughing as I approached the flat. Yamilia and Rosa were sitting together, beers on the table, lifelong friends, all smiles and camaraderie.

'Ay, mi amor,' said Yamilia, 'where you go? I think you go home to England and leave us here.'

Rosa laughed as though this was the best joke she'd ever heard, told by the best friend she'd ever had. I didn't reply, walked into the kitchen to get a drink. The fridge was full. With beer and rum were fresh cuts of meat, chosen with care at a Havana market; fruit and vegetables filled the wooden rack next to the fridge. I poured a long glass of rum and diluted it with ice, lime juice and soda water. I sat next to Rosa, opposite Yamilia and smiled.

'You look good, mi amor,' she said. 'You have health. You go to the beach?'

She looked great, carefree, the way she looked with her mother in Lugareno. An unwanted thought sprang into my mind – how men, all of us as far as I can tell, are fooled by beauty. Why did I believe in this woman? A woman I knew to be a liar and, although she could lift my spirits, was capable of destroying me. Because she radiated an energy that engulfed me, so that I just wanted to be there, in that place with her. It wasn't even anything to do with sex, I was just happy in her company. But why? Why indeed.

'I went to Santiago de Cuba with José,' I said, deciding to begin with the truth, or at least some of it. 'And I went to Trinidad, alone.'

Her smile didn't waver, although her eyes flashed at José's name. Rosa interrupted.

'You like Santiago?'

'It's hot,' I said, 'but now I have a business. I can make some money.'

I explained about the cars.

'That's good, Chris,' said Yamilia, clearly uninterested, 'is important for you to make money here.'

I saw no sign of resentment. It looked as though we were friends again, starting over. Even José wasn't off limits.

'So you go with José? And Celia? She come too?'

This with a smile.

'Yes, José's girlfriend came too.'

She nodded thoughtfully at this.

'Si. The girlfriend of José.'

She spoke quickly in Spanish to Rosa, who nodded

thoughtfully before replying with something I didn't understand. They nodded sagely to each other. To change the subject I brought up the rent; it was overdue although Rosa was cool. I started to count out enough for three months. Yamilia caught my eye and shook her head. I paid Rosa for a month, waiting to see what Yamilia was up to.

When Rosa left Yamilia put on some music and took a shower. She came back with a towel round her and danced to the music. Eventually she let the towel slip to the floor, pulled me out of the chair and danced close, holding my eyes, hers full of amusement and something else. She stroked my erection as she danced, then slowly undressed me. I felt stupid dancing with my stiffy bouncing around, but when I tried to stop she said,

'No, mi amor, dance. Dance with *me*.'

We danced. She went to her knees and took me in her mouth for just a few seconds then moved away, dancing and laughing, completely unselfconscious of her own body movement, or she backed onto me allowing me inside her briefly, all the time in a personal rhythm with the music. After an hour of this I would have come regardless of physical contact, so pumped up I could hardly stand it. She knew me though, and as I was about to come she fell to her knees and took me in her mouth again until I was drained and sank to the cool tiles. A bonding session. She would stay. For now.

We lazed around for a while, spending most days at the pool and the evenings at home, both happy it seemed to let any conflict take a break. Tony phoned and invited us for a meal at his house. The invite could only be a prelude to business. He could help I was sure; he also wanted to make money, and Yamilia wanted a house at least. However, I didn't have to agree to anything with anyone, so I settled into an easygoing acceptance for the time being. It was easier on the nerves and, anyway, I was learning. There was a danger that this could be taken for weakness, but if I said no in the right places I thought I'd be OK. So we went to Tony's.

We took a taxi. I tried to stop using hire cars. José wrote one off and nearly killed us when I allowed him to drive me to Matanzas. Rentacar were very laid back about it and just offered me another, but taxis seemed a safer option for now. Tony's place was halfway between Villa Pan Americana and the prospective house in Guanabacoa. If Yamilia knew anything about the purpose of the meal or had any ulterior motive herself she hid it behind a flood of small talk. Tony lived in a medium-sized, one storey house with a large dining room, kitchen, bathroom and two bedrooms. It was fairly new, clean, breezy and affluent, but on a busy street that rarely let up on noise. Not that noise seemed to bother any Cuban I knew. It was a fact of life.

Tony greeted me with hugs, old friends already. He was cooking and damp with sweat. His wife, Adela, a plump jolly woman, was equally welcoming. She poured beers and, after showing me due respect and establishing her lack of English, she chatted happily to Yamilia and showed her the house. I took my beer to the back yard where a lean, healthy Doberman patrolled. Tony served up the meal: chicken, rice, black beans and plantain. Conversation at first was limited by my Spanish, vaguely skirting my plans for the future. Yamilia told her stories, exaggerating wildly, and the meal ticked along pleasantly, the food good and the beers topped up.

After the meal we sat in the late evening sun in the front garden, talking above the noise of the traffic. Yamilia deferred to Tony and kept an eye on me, pleased because we drank only beer. Later we sat on the patio. Yamilia was needed to translate, although she would never have stayed out of this conversation.

Tony spoke clearly, in measured tones. If he was lying, he was a practised, skilful liar. Most Cubans talk to each other as if they're twenty yards apart and both deaf. He spoke softly. Whatever Tony was, he was a professional. He said that, legally, I could not own a house; my name could never go on the paperwork. But if I was happy to live in the house, the owner and master to all intents and purposes, then that could be arranged. Of course we would have to decide whose name would go on the paperwork. He glanced at Yamilia and then at me, the implication clear. Although Tony had shown nothing but politeness, courtesy and respect to Yamilia, I sensed a different question in his eyes: Do you really trust this woman? Are you sure about this? Was I happy for Yamilia's name to go on the paperwork? He held my eyes for a few seconds longer than necessary. Yamilia watched us.

'You will arrange everything?' I said.

'Si,' he said, still holding my eyes.

Yamilia, unable to stay quiet, added her own 'Si'.

'Si,' I said, without looking at Yamilia, 'you take care of everything.'

We couldn't move into the new house for two months,

time for the paperwork to be done and the occupants to leave for Spain. Tony owned three houses, one which he rented to tourists. Yamilia wanted us to leave Rosa's and move there until the house was ready. She said it was better, the rent less and that we would show good faith with Tony.

I called Paul

'I'm going to buy that house.'

'Good idea. I said before, do it.'

'It's complicated. It may not even end up being my house.'

'Do it. It will be a base for now.'

'I like the place. Tony seems OK. He knows people at the right level. You'll meet him.'

'Good.

'He doesn't approve of drinking. It interferes with business. He likes money.'

'Splendid.'

'What time do you arrive?'

I bring to my life a certain amount of mess.
Francis Ford Coppola

PAUL VISITS

I waited with José at the airport for hours, long after the stragglers whose luggage took longest to surface. I assumed Paul had changed his mind. We were about to leave when he walked unsteadily into arrivals. He'd tripped over someone's luggage and been detained. Whatever security made of him the decision must have been something like 'English drunk, but harmless and will spend money.'

'So, free at last.'

'Viva Cuba Libre. Is the bar open? I need a drink.'

He had put on weight since I'd last seen him. A big man with short, thinning fair hair, he'd been slim and almost athletic in prison. Now he carried a significant paunch and seemed to lean forward as he walked, dragged along by it; he was still handsome, carried authority with his size, confidence and booming public school voice, but seemed permanently red-faced, a professional drinker's face.

At the house Yamilia greeted him politely in English, shared a drink with us and, seeing our condition, suggested we might like to sleep. We didn't. As she walked to our bedroom Paul said,

'*Now* I understand why you're here.'

Yamilia ignored José's presence when we arrived. When he was still there in the morning, showing no signs of leaving, her mood changed. She seemed confused, not knowing how to behave in front of Paul and irritated by José, who clearly liked him and enjoyed his frequent, easy laughter. Yamilia behaved as she pleased in front of me. Now, unsure if she should be polite, desperately trying to read this new, strange, male presence, she didn't know what to do, covering her discomfort by fussing around us, offering coffee, drinks, food and tidying obsessively.

It didn't help that José was enjoying himself so much. Our conversation centred on how I'd got to Cuba: Paul's time in prison, his previous arrests, our meetings and plans, and a few close calls on the way. José understood and joined in with some stories of his own. That's all it was, boy's stuff. But Yamilia, excluded, her English not up to this, saw things differently. She saw conversation and laughter. She saw me and José and a new guest talking and laughing, and then laughing some more. And she didn't know what it was about. And José did. Was he telling stories about her? She flashed glances at me, perhaps for help. I saw the signs, but did nothing. She was boiling up to something. I wanted to see it. And I wanted Paul to see it too.

When it arrived it was directed at José. Although José had said nothing about her to either me or Paul, she clearly imagined otherwise, that he'd been talking about her, and not in a good way. She pointed at him, walked to his chair and wagged her finger in his face, flounced away and returned, laughed contemptuously at a joke of her own as she listed his faults. She shook her head at the image he

145

portrayed and the naivety of Paul, and especially me, for associating with such a man. Hands on hips she reeled off his crimes to Paul, who, fascinated but not understanding a word, listened with polite attention. He appeared to want to nod or shake his head, but was afraid to choose wrongly, so he remained still, smiling and blinking. Rosa stood in the kitchen doorway, arms folded, watching.

Receiving only rapt silence in response, Yamilia shook her head angrily, black hair flying, and gestured scornfully at the air for not understanding her, a dismissive huff as she condemned us to our stupidity. She wasn't going to lower herself to explain if we were *that* stupid. The more she shouted the angrier she got, the hurricane began inside her, her hair seemed to take on electricity, her eyes flashed, she moved in a jerky, yet graceful manner and we stared at her transfixed. Of course she misunderstood, took it as a sign of disagreement and got even angrier, on and on, a hurricane that would have to blow itself out.

'Hmmm,' said Paul, 'beautiful woman. Stroppy bitch, though.'

The room was silent for a few seconds, expressions frozen as people absorbed what had happened, as though in the aftermath of an exploding TV or surprising flatulence. Yamilia looked at Paul as if he had suddenly appeared by magic.

'What he say?'

José, cockier than usual and clearly having enjoyed her performance in company, rather than just at him, or me, said

'He says you are beautiful.'

I was grateful that he either did not understand, or had

decided not to translate, stroppy bitch. She stared at him and then at Paul, unmoving. I had the impression that if I touched her there would be a crackle of static and a mild shock. Paul hadn't taken his eyes from her, perhaps expecting an encore, a look of mild wonderment on his face as though he expected her to burst into song or produce a dove from somewhere. And Yamilia was suddenly aware of a roomful of people, silent and staring. At her. She muttered to herself, tossed her hair and headed for the door. Nobody jumped at the thunderous slam. We were expecting it.

'She's left you again,' said Paul.

I realised that I knew what she would do. She would spend the day with Lucia or Eliza or someone else. She wouldn't go to Havana, not with new male company in the flat and José making himself at home. She would complain first and then banish whatever had caused the outburst from her mind. Then she would change the subject, talk, laugh and make herself happy. Then, probably in the early evening, because we were bound to go out, she would return, full of smiles as though nothing had happened. And, in her mind, nothing would have happened. It would not just have been buried. It would be forgotten. History. No importante.

'She will come back,' said José.

She returned after a few hours armed with supplies: food, rum and cigarettes. She greeted José as though he had just arrived and joined in, one of the boys, drinking rum after rum much too fast, before suddenly announcing that she was taking a siesta. Her unsubtle glance in my direction showed that she expected me to join her, if only temporarily. Afterwards she swallowed a diazepam and fell into a deep sleep within a minute. Glad that she was back on a vaguely even keel, I was also glad we were free of her company for a while; she wouldn't wake now until the next day.

Paul boasted of his prowess at chess, tried to get me to play, but I don't have the patience or the skill.

'José plays chess,' I said.

Paul seemed insulted by the very suggestion, but eventually they played. José sat, calmly sipping his rum, making his moves after brief consideration and waiting patiently while Paul, red-faced and sweating, interminably pondered his replies. It was all over in twenty painful minutes. Later José said,

'This man cannot play chess.'

Paul never mentioned chess again.

I showed him around Havana. We dropped José at his flat and drove along the malecon; I showed him where Fidel made his speeches in front of the US embassy. He only looked up when I pointed something out; otherwise he stared straight ahead or at passing women, who appeared not to impress him. He held a bottle of white rum between his knees, sipping regularly. We headed for Old Havana and the cathedral.

'Can we look at Cubacel?' he said.

'Why?'

'I just want to see it.'

It was just a large private house, converted for purpose, and close to where the rich lived. He stared at the building in the way Japanese tourists stare at historic sites. If he'd had a camera he'd have taken a photograph.

'We need to see if we can get you free calls.'

'Not here.'

'I know how to do it.'

'Believe me, not here.'

You didn't cheat people like Cubacel. Free calls could be had, but not here. I had used people who could tap into phone lines and gave thirty minutes call time from their homes for ten dollars, but it was fiddly and only available at certain times. I was too lazy to bother and used my cellular.

We drove to Cathedral Square, quiet and peaceful in the fading light. When we were settled with our drinks he began to talk about women, asking about the racial mix. He sat hunched, his head forward, obsessively, unconsciously, touching his scalp where his hair was thinning, as though encouraging it to stay, or come back.

'So what is the proportion here,' he said, 'black to white?'

'It's hard to say. I think officially it's sixty percent white Spanish descent and forty Afro-Caribbean from the slaves.'

'And is it?'

'I don't know. In Havana it seems more like fifty-fifty, perhaps whiter in the country. But it's not as simple as that. The Russians were here for thirty years; that must have had its effect. There's a Chinatown. This was a playground to the Americans for fifty years. I don't know. They're a good-looking people though, whatever their lineage.'

'Hmm, I don't see much whiteness.'

He meant pale, English winter, never see the sun, pale.

'It's a semi-tropical country. That's the sun.'

I'd seen photographs of Paul's ex-wife, pale, blonde and buxom. He also admired similar looking singers and actors. I began to realise that there might not be much here for him.

'So what's Yamilia?'

'Her mother is black. Her father is a light-skinned Haitian.'

'So she's mulata?'

'No. But she's fairly light-skinned. So is one of her sisters.'

'So there's white in her. A sugar baron from the good old days?'

'I don't know. She is what she is.'

The square was dominated by the cathedral on one side; the restaurant and houses made up the other three. A Unesco site, protected for its beauty and historical significance, the houses, with balconies overlooking the square contained ordinary Cubans, comparable to renting a council house in St Peter's Square or the French Quarter in New Orleans; the houses would be worth millions in almost any other country.

I was irritated that Paul hadn't noticed where we were, that he hadn't commented on one of my favourite places. The light hadn't quite given up for the day; the sun beyond the square was sinking fast towards the sea. A flock of small birds took off from the roof of the cathedral and flew towards their roosting place across the red stained clouds in a fading sky. This was the quiet time, the tourists brushing up for the evening, the interval between day and night, two very different worlds, musicians taking a break, birds chattering, grackles squabbling for overnight perches in the trees.

'Have you noticed where you are?'

He raised his head slowly, looked blearily first at me and then beyond and around. A childish smile creased his face. For a moment the square was almost silent.

'Hmm. Splendid,' he said.

'So what are you going to do with Yamilia?'

'See how it goes.'

'Do you love her?'

'Yes.'

'But?'

'I won't mess things up because of her, if that's what you mean.'

'Good man.'

Paul's first thought on rising was another drink, whereas back then, mine was for food and a certain recovery time before starting again. Paul didn't like food. He drank a strange mixture of rum, wine and beer, starting very early and just sipping all day. He was happy around the flat, playing his CDs or fiddling with my laptop, but never at ease when we went out. Then he seemed overwhelmed, uncomfortable, only relaxing at the top hotels where the people were familiar to him, the same people in top hotels everywhere, functional and predictable.

Paul was thirty-eight then. He laughed often, easily and loudly; a thorough cynic, his only pleasures appeared to be defrauding financial institutions and drinking. Unfortunately the two didn't always gel and, although very smart on how to part banks from their money he was beginning, with age, to make drunken mistakes. His last two years in prison had probably saved his life; a doctor there told him that he wouldn't last long if he continued to drink.

During our prison meetings he'd been clear-headed and sharp, planning my escape meticulously and efficiently. He was brilliant then and that's how I remembered him. Now, two stone heavier, pink-faced and hesitant, I saw the man who had managed to get himself arrested twice. On both occasions he may as well have walked into a police station and confessed. His cool confidence had gone, replaced by a jovial shiftiness. I didn't believe he'd obtained an ABTA, our licence to be travel agents. I doubted he'd done much at all connected with business. He'd thought of a name and designed a logo – the fun parts – but as yet no ABTA and no customers. His days in England began in whatever hotel he happened to be in and progressed no further than the bar. Perhaps when he was younger he'd had spectacular successes while drinking too, but he couldn't do it now, and he didn't know it. Anybody who met him knew he was an alcoholic within two hours. It didn't matter to them. He was good company, talked easily to anybody and stayed on his feet – he didn't fall over or became stroppy and embarrassing. And being Cuban they naturally assumed he was wealthy, like all Europeans. But could he run a business from England?

We had some fun; he enjoyed the attention he received from everyone who took care of him. Tony liked him. We had a meeting at his house and although Tony disapproved of drinking, he must have assumed that whatever our condition, we were here, we were rich, so we must be able to function like this. He even took a couple of rums himself and smoked a cigarette. And Paul liked him. Tony knew things: politics, banking, tourism, crime, women, and business. He knew what could be done, what we could get away with and Paul was impressed. But not, I thought, impressed enough to do anything about it. As I watched, probably as drunk as Paul, I thought he was just drifting, drifting from one situation to another and not really conscious of a past or a future, as long as a bottle remained by his side.

His parents were rich. If all went badly for him he must have known, at least subconsciously, that he would never fall completely, never be alone, never be really and truly without money. But it could happen to me. Nobody was ready to catch me if I fell. And while I decided that we would still have a go at this (what choice did I have?), I also decided there, as I watched Paul roar at another joke and sip his rum, that I was on my own. And now I would have to think and behave accordingly.

Paul's booming, confident voice and laugh attracted Yamilia's attention. I often caught her looking at him, trying to figure out what was behind the voice. He was much younger than me. Did he have more money? Who was the better bet here? But apart from wistful looks as she moved around the flat, he took little notice of her. During his second week he spent more time with José than me because they both liked to visit the top hotels. I understood José's liking for them, he couldn't get into them without an invitation from a tourist, but to me the hotels were the same the world over – a slight Cuban flavour with the music – otherwise very dull.

One night we went to the club at the Villa Pan Americana hotel. I realised in Paul's company that it was nothing, just a large room with a bar, but that with the company of Yamilia, cheerful lighting, great music and rum it had become much more in my eyes. Paul may have imagined places like the Tropicana, tourist brochure images of long legged beauties, smiling faces and sparkly outfits. Here was a place you could find in most towns and cities in the UK – just a hall with music. Of course it was the people, the atmosphere, a unique love of life in the moment that made me love it. Paul was oblivious to the atmosphere. So far he didn't much like the people and he hated the music. We saw Cuba through different eyes.

At the airport he drank so much that I feared they wouldn't let him on the plane. At security he wobbled and smiled at the female official as she checked his visa. She fired some questions at him, presumably in Spanish, because he shrugged and laughed. She turned and stared hard at us, where we watched from a few yards away. Then she considered for a few seconds before noisily stamping his visa, handing him his passport and unlocking the door to departures.

'Bring me some books,' I shouted, before he disappeared.

'What sort of books?'

The security official stared fiercely between us.

'Detective fiction, anything.'

'OK. Pip, pip,' he said, and vanished through the door.

I took José to his flat and drove home. Yamilia was watching a film when I arrived. I poured a rum and joined her.

'Paul go?' she said.

'Si. He will come back in a few weeks to meet Rumbos.'

She shook her head.

'You will never have success with this man.'

In heaven all the interesting people are missing.
Nietzsczhe

TONY'S HOUSE

I bought the house. A condition of Tony's help was that
we move into one of his properties while we waited for
everything to be finalised with the new house. Yamilia
wanted to move, preferring Tony's. It was closer to the
property we were buying. She said that Tony would look
after us, introduce me to people and help me with whatever
I wanted to do. It was also much cheaper. Hard to argue
with the logic. But I didn't want to move; I liked Rosa's.
Rosa was distraught. She appealed to me, voiced the doubts
that troubled me. Yamilia dismissed her with a contemptuous wave,

'It's not your problem, Rosa,' she said.

And we were gone.

Tony's house sat in a row of one-storey villas, white with
small neat front lawns. Inside it proved to be L-shaped,
the long part going back deep into a luscious garden of
long grass, plants and fruit trees. Three bedrooms, a
kitchen, lounge and two bathrooms jutted from different
parts of the L, the whole surrounded by a high wire fence,
padlocked at the front and guarded by Dingo, a seven-year-

old Doberman. Fifteen dollars a day. I paid Rosa twenty-five. Perhaps it was a good move after all.

Tony's ancient TV gave off sparks and minor electric shocks, so I went into Havana to buy a new one. Every shop in Havana had run out of TVs, just empty windows and display areas. I knew they had been fully stocked only days before. The assistants were reluctant to explain the absence. Tony laughed when I told him:

'Is Fidel,' he said.

According to Tony's sources Fidel had decided that all schools should have one TV for every six students. In one weekend he cleared the shops and made it happen. I'd have to wait until some more were imported from China.

We had local shops, a good local bar where I could play pool and new friends. Tony visited every day, firstly to feed Dingo, who was fed on scraps once a day – bread, cereal, chunks of bone with slivers of meat remaining. Tony was no kinder to animals than most Cubans, not cruel, just indifferent. Dingo roamed where a fifteen-foot chain allowed him. He was never released from the chain, not by Tony anyway. After feeding Dingo he made coffee, tiny cups of strong, black, Cuban coffee. He watched wide-eyed as Yamilia poured mine into a large white mug.

'Ay, Chris, mucho cafe,' he said.

As we sipped our coffee he talked and after a while I didn't need Yamilia's rough translations. Tony spoke very slowly and expressively. That and my bad Spanish got us by. He served during the missile crisis in 1962, an event that caught my imagination as a child and aroused my curiosity about Cuba, about Castro and what on earth was going on there. The whole world expected to be annihilated at any moment as Kennedy, Castro and Khrushchev played poker with the world's future, nuclear weapons at the ready. Tony manned an anti-aircraft gun on the malecon as a fifteen-year-old while they waited for the US attack that never came. Highly intelligent, he understood the politics, was a firm believer in the revolution until he didn't believe in it anymore, when he became what he was now: fixer, a dealer – a businessman.

We talked every day. What were my plans? What would I like to do? Cuba was good for business. And when Fidel finally went – well, anything would be possible. And to be in early, like me – I could do very well in Cuba. We often visited his house for dinner, where his wife, and sometimes Tony, cooked. The Doberman there roamed free, was sleek and healthy. Why had Dingo drawn the short straw? Sometimes we ate out at restaurants of Tony's choosing.

We met his mother in Havana. She had the top two floors of a large old building on a quiet street in Old Havana. It was well maintained, in contrast to most of the city's colonial Spanish architecture, which crumbled as fast as it could be restored. Some of his large family had gathered there; a sister, Elizabeth, I'd already met in Guanabacoa. Another sister, Loli, visited from Las Palmas with her husband. Tony's mother, white-haired, fit and bright-eyed, had an imperious air about her. I exchanged glances with Yamilia. We were up for inspection.

As we were shown the house I thought of Andy, the American. The house was full of antique furniture and paintings, chandeliers hung from the ceiling – pre-revolution stuff they'd managed to hold on to. Yamilia was at her most demure, which didn't suit her at all; their politeness towards her frayed at the edges. Tony initiated a strange conversation, for my benefit I thought, about the film *Fresa y Chocolate*, Strawberry and Chocolate. Cuba was slowly coming to terms with homosexuality. I think because I occasionally read books they decided I must be an intellectual. Tony led the conversation as I watched their faces. Loli joined in, showing a spark of interest. Tony's mother stared straight ahead as though a bad smell had appeared beneath her nose and Lisdey, Loli's husband, a veteran of the Cuban campaign in Angola was utterly baffled, nodding, shaking his head or smiling when he thought it appropriate. Tony tried to include me in the conversation.

'Si Tony, entiende,' I said, '*Fresa y Chocolat*, metro sexual y macho.'

Yamilia spoke gravely, as though discussing someone with a terminal disease, of a female newsreader who was reputedly a lesbian. She said later that Loli had taken her aside, lectured her about the great opportunity she had, how she must learn to change her behaviour. That she accepted the lecture without protest was a minor miracle and I wished she hadn't.

Tony decided that we needed a good translator. Yamilia was OK, José was better, but neither could handle complexities, and Tony wanted to be clear. Manolo, around thirty and married with a young son, was the first unsmiling Cuban I'd ever met. His English was perfect. He also spoke fluent French and German, was obviously well-educated and slightly condescending to the company he was forced to keep, including me. He irritably corrected my Spanish and sighed at my pidgin style. But he understood the little nuances of our conversations, both ways – subtle, important things. I was surprised that he'd never left the country. He said he had a German girlfriend, who he could go and live with any time he liked, but wouldn't leave his wife and child. I didn't believe he'd ever leave Cuba. There was a depressive air about him, as though he thought most actions pointless. I saw his wife rarely; she was slim, pale and pretty and didn't smile either. She never spoke to me. During our gatherings she ensconced herself with the girls and that was that.

Manolo's translations changed everything. I'd relied on hazy at best versions of events, that and my own instincts. Now Manolo interpreted every word, caught shades of meaning lost before. Now I could have conversations with Tony about politics, life, women – anything. As long as Manolo was around. And he was often around. He didn't work and he certainly wasn't well-off, but neither did he seem bothered about money. Painfully direct, he said exactly what he thought regardless of potential offence. I thought he was more honest than Tony would have liked – but how could he know? – Manolo controlled our conversations. Only he understood everything. He had the power, and to an extent he gave me some of that power. I asked Tony about payment for Manolo. He shrugged as though it was of no importance. I doubted this, but let it go. It was a big mistake.

Manolo did what he was told. I know he got nothing from Tony (few people did) and he never asked for anything from me directly. I paid for food, rum, taxis, the odd book, but I never gave him money – he was just around and I took him for granted. We needed Manolo when we shopped for the new house. Yamilia loved the process of shopping and would have dragged it out for weeks, but these were large purchases and I needed to be present. I don't like shopping, and with Yamilia slowing things down and me speeding them up we managed to get the basics: bed, fridge, cooker, bookcases, a couple of armchairs and sundries in a few days. That must have been a tiresome task for Manolo.

Despite Tony's enthusiasm for my presence in Cuba and the financial prospects, he shipped increasing numbers of his family out of the country, often to Spain. My purchase of the house had helped send a nephew and his wife to Las Palmas. Tony had no interest in leaving. He liked Cuba, loved the constant struggle with the CDR, bureaucracy and the government in pursuit of money and a decent living. Tough-minded, ruthless and hardworking, it was a struggle he usually won. I asked Yamilia how ordinary Cubans lived, about their earnings and allowances. I gathered the average worker earned around ten dollars a month, working alternate days to maintain full employment. A doctor or a scientist might earn forty. So the honest Cubans, outside the tourist industry, the ones who accepted their role and took the basic food allowances – how did they live?

'They eat shit,' said Yamilia.

Tony liked José at first. He didn't know about his problems with the police, that he didn't have a driving licence or that he exerted little influence on me. I think he respected José's knowledge of life in Havana, something he'd lost touch with below the higher levels. He trusted him then, thought of him as protection for me, someone to keep me from the wrong places or people and, he hoped, to tell him what was happening, what I was thinking. So at least for now, while Yamilia wanted to make the right impression with Tony, she had to tolerate José. It was comical to see them feigning friendship and respect.

Sunday afternoons became a boy's gathering at the round dining table, Tony's day off from business for gossip, politics, stories – anything. Yamilia occasionally listened in case we said anything interesting, but, finding that we didn't, she played music or watched TV. Tony was curious about life in England. He had mixed reports from the relatives he helped to leave for Spain and the USA. They were surprised how hard life could be, how difficult to get started without friends or relatives and, most of all, the unfriendliness, the general lack of welcome or care. Many Cubans believed in the satellite images beamed into hotels of happy consumers in the lands of plenty. Yamilia and José both assumed I lived a life of wealthy ease in Europe.

Although many of the young, especially in the cities, were frustrated, I found that generally Castro had wide support. It certainly isn't true that the whole population is itching to escape. A few weeks before I'd landed at Jose Marti airport from Las Palmas, where I spent a week with Paul. The plane was full of Cubans returning home or visiting. It was late afternoon as the island came into sight: expanses of golden sand, rolling white breakers and green palms. They rushed to the windows, punching their fists and shouting: 'Cuba, Cuba, Cuba'. I tried without success to imagine the same happening at Heathrow.

Although the embargo was crippling, Cuba did slowly progress. They traded with those countries not totally in thrall to the USA and tourism increased year by year.

'So where does the money go?' I asked Tony.

'Chris, Fidel is political, the people get the minimum he thinks they need – education, medicine, culture if they want it. There is a little more scope for entrepreneurs, paladares, family businesses but Fidel is more interested in supplying doctors for Nicaragua, Columbia and Venezuela or supporting revolutions elsewhere.'

'For money, oil?'

'Fidel only care about money,' said José.

'But not for himself, José,' said Tony, 'for the economy. He wants political change in Venezuela, Central America, South America. He has no interest in personal wealth, although not all in the government are the same. He is a Marxist, his beliefs have never changed. Of course he is also a ruthless dictator. We could not have this conversation in a public bar.'

In her book, *The Country Under My Skin*, Gioconda Belli describes her visit to Cuba in 1978 with fellow Nicaraguan revolutionaries. She admired Castro, but resented what she saw as his desire to meddle with the Sandinista revolution, a need to take control. She also claimed he made a clumsy seduction attempt disguised as a request for political discussion.

José was not impressed. The money was not reaching him, his only concern.

'The young of Havana don't give a shit about the health of the Nicaraguan people,' said Manolo,' they just want what they see on hotel TVs. American culture does more damage than its bombs.'

'And trade is improved,' said Tony, ignoring him, 'rice from Vietnam, TVs from China, cars from Germany, Japan, Korea and France. Oil from Venezuela and now we have medical tourism. Many people come here for the clinics. Fidel spends much on medical research.'

That was true. Later I'd be treated in one as a favour for Tony. It was full of affluent foreign visitors seeking a cure for their ailments – there was a waiting list.

'We don't have a problem with drugs or racism. Women are equal...'

Yamilia snorted derisively at this from the kitchen. Tony pretended not to hear,

'...Cuba has a vibrant culture, a sense of community, a common identity.'

Yamilia danced past the table singing,

'We are the world, we are the people.'

Manolo, I suspected at Tony's prompting, tried to introduce me to beer. I didn't like the popular brand, Cristal, so he suggested Hatuey, after first mocking my pronunciation. It's pronounced: Atway. A bottled beer, it was best drunk chilled. On the label was a small Indian against a colourful rural background.

'Hatuey was a Dominican Indian,' said Manolo. 'All Cuba and Dominica was Indian. The Spanish killed them all. They fought, but they were too small and didn't have the weapons, the fighting experience or the wickedness. Hatuey came here and organised the few Indians left alive and, for a while, they had some success. Then they caught him. They burned him.'

'So he's a hero?'

'Yes. When they were about to burn him, they asked him if he wanted to convert to the Catholic religion.'

' "Why?" he asked them.

' "Because if you don't you will not go to heaven," they said.

' "Heaven?" he asked.

' "Yes, paradise."

' "Will the Spanish be there?" he asked.

' "Yes."

' "Then I don't want to go," he said. And they burned him.'

I liked the story and drank the beer for a while. It was good beer, better than Cristal, but hard to find, something to do with the copyright of Hatuey's name. Anyway, it was just the story that attracted me; I don't like beer and I soon went back to rum.

Manolo's German girlfriend arrived for a visit. She stayed at a casa particular in Villa Pan Americana. They talked a great deal in German and Spanish, but appeared not to have a physical relationship. I met her at Lucia's one day; I don't know why she was there. We went for a coffee. Blonde with pale blue eyes, she was very pale, but exuded robust health, Aryan.

'You don't see much of Manolo,' I said

'I'm not really here for Manolo. I keep returning, but not for Manolo now, he's just useful. Why are you here?'

Very direct.

'It's fun. Why are you here?'

'The same, it's fun, it's different, unique. The men.'

I remembered a conversation with Yamilia at a baseball game. I had noticed a striking blonde sitting with a crowd of Cubans. I asked Yamilia if the woman was Cuban. She looked her over scornfully and said:

'She is Swede. She come here to fuck big black man. In her own country she would look like this at those men.'

She held her nose, lifted her chin and put on a haughty expression of superiority.

'Here she is different, nobody can see her. She wants to fuck black men with big pingas.'

'And you are here for Yamilia?' she said.

'Sort of. She was the catalyst.'

She snorted.

'Did you find it shocking at first, the sex here?'

'You mean the biting and scratching, the roughness of it?'

'Not so much that, the talk, and the things they say. It surprised me the first time.'

I stared blankly.

'You don't know? Oh, my god,' she buried her face in her hands, 'the language?'

I waited.

'For men I don't know, but "you fucking whore, I'm going to fuck you until you can't walk straight", "come here you whore, bitch – do this, do that", you don't know about that, you don't do that with Yamilia, the others? I've heard the women say that European men treat them like glass, as though they might break, that they're shy and don't know what they want.'

'A bit, she's rough. I don't like the roughness much,

165

sometimes, but not much. I say some things when I feel like it; I hear some stuff, mostly in Spanish.'

'Of course, your Spanish is not good. You've been here a long time. Why is that?'

'Yamilia, José, Manolo, Lucia, Raul, they all speak pretty good English. I want to learn, I try, but we always end up speaking English. It's just easier.'

'You must learn. You won't get the most out of life here until you do.'

'I'd like to and I've tried, but I don't think I'm good with other languages, and they speak so fast here. The rough language, you like it?'

'Sure, it's healthy, I give the same back. You learn that here, get everything off your chest, out of your mind, keep it clean. It's such a healthy way of life. Always contradictions, but healthy. They are always talking, shouting, moving, living in the moment. It's good for the soul.'

Laura: 'We must be sensible.'
Alec: 'It's too late now to be sensible and all that.'
Brief Encounter

JEALOUSY

Yamilia was often jealous. I liked it – if she was jealous she must care. If she caught me looking at other women she said 'You like?' and shook her head at my denials. What annoyed her more was women looking at me, often completely misunderstanding their reasons. She was once extremely rude to a young American woman who was just enquiring how I got my phone and how she could get one. Most of all she was jealous of José. Jealous of his hold on my friendship, his hold on my time and the value I gave his opinion. Her attempts at peace never lasted long and Celia, guilty by association, suffered too.

We had planned to meet José and Celia at the Latin American stadium for a Saturday night game. At the very last minute she decided she didn't want to go. I thought she enjoyed these nights, which involved rum and music and humour no matter what the quality of the game, but now she insisted that she hated it and wasn't going. And if she wasn't going she didn't want me to go either. I told her I was going.

'To see your friend José. You fuck José?'

'That's stupid. You were supposed to be coming and Celia will be there.'

'You fuck Celia?'

I called a taxi from my cellular.

'You think me stupid?'

She advanced as if intending to hit me, her face a picture of manufactured indignation.

'You think me stupid?'

She wanted a confrontation.

'I'm going,' I said, and walked into the front garden to wait for the taxi.

I'd worn a suit because we were going to a club afterwards. It was a very hot, breezeless evening and I was already beginning to sweat. The intention had been to take an air-conditioned taxi to the game, where the stadium would be cool and I could remove my jacket, then wear it at the club where the extreme air-conditioning would make it welcome. I hadn't meant to wait around like this. Yamilia came out, put her arms around my waist and smiled. As I relaxed she grabbed my wallet from inside the jacket. I caught her as she tried to run into the house. She went into a crouch, gripping my wallet in two hands. I tried to prise it from her, but although stronger than her I couldn't separate all her fingers at once, her grip was tight like a claw, and she constantly turned away from me. My wallet crumpled in her grip, bending my passport and cards.

'You no go,' she said, repeating it over and over.

The taxi arrived. The driver got out, leaned against his car and watched us.

'Momento,' I shouted.

He shrugged. I was out of breath and sweating. I could already smell myself just a few minutes after showering. And my enthusiasm for the night out was gone. Yamilia shouted at the driver telling him to go.

'You sure?' he said in English.

'No. Wait,' I shouted back.

She still had my wallet and without knocking her unconscious I couldn't see any way of getting it. I put my hand in my back pocket. She saw my intention and sprang at me. I left my hand in the pocket around the money there so she couldn't reach it and moved toward the taxi. She bit me hard on the shoulder and hung on for a few seconds before I pushed her away. Only when I got the gate unlocked did she give up.

In the back of the taxi I wiped her saliva from my sleeve. Her teeth had dented the fabric and my arm stung. I tried to hide my breathlessness and anger from the driver whose eyes studied me in the rear view mirror.

'Fiery woman,' he said cheerfully, 'strong.'

'Si.'

'Women, eh? What can you do?'

I turned and looked out of the window. I could hear my breathing, feel my heart beat, my chest rose and fell. The driver turned on his radio and hummed to himself for the rest of the journey.

I had about eighty dollars in my pocket. José would pay in pesos for the game, but we didn't have enough for the club, where entrance alone was twenty-five dollars. I didn't want to go now anyway.

'What's up?' said José when we met up.

I told him.

'You are crazy man.'

I took regular sips from our bottle of rum, barely watching the game, sinking deeper and deeper into resentment. I didn't want to; I fought against it and would have been happy if I could. Nothing would have shaken this off better than a good night out – we could have still got drunk somewhere else, but the game, the company and the entertainment made no difference.

'I'm going,' I said.

I gave them some money for drinks and left. I took a taxi to central Havana and sat in a tourist bar, watching the game I'd just left, on TV. I stared at the screen without seeing it, brooding on the ruined evening. The barman tried conversation and gave up. My bad temper made me worse tempered, my anger made me angrier. I remembered every false accusation and every tantrum. What had amused or delighted me before became sinister, good times became bad times and optimism turned to pessimism.

I drank for hours, moving from bar to bar to avoid conversation. The rum had little effect. I replayed the fight, the spoilt, smug, child-like expression, the crumpled passport, the heat of my body and the smell of sweat. I slowed down, tried deep breaths, attempted perspective without success. I thought about a woman and revenge, but for once that didn't appeal. I wanted to book into a hotel, but I needed my passport. The fact that I had to go back to her hurt me physically. I ran into a few people I knew. I allowed my expression and my silence to deter them.

When I had only my taxi fare left I headed home. As the taxi stopped in front of the house I caught her silhouetted in the bedroom window. The bathroom light is left on all night and its glow shadowed her as she approached the window and then stepped quickly back. I felt suddenly calm. I took my time paying the driver and kept my eye on the window as I unlocked the gate. Dingo barked his warning to the intruder. I unlocked the door. She could have locked me out with the latch, but hadn't. I walked through to the back patio to quieten Dingo. I glanced into the bedroom as I passed, a solitary foot hung over a corner of the bed.

My calmness had caused my appetite to return; I hadn't eaten for hours. I made a sandwich, drank half a litre of water and some more rum before giving the scraps to Dingo. She lay naked, face down on the bed with one fan keeping the mosquitoes away. Her eyes were closed, her breath feigning sleep. I cleaned my teeth and undressed. Her legs were slightly parted. I used my knees to push them apart and slid straight into her. She was already wet. I pulled her onto her knees, spread her juice around her ass and fucked her there. Normally I would have been slow and gentle, waiting for her to accept me, but now I moved hard and fast. She raised herself up onto her hands and watched me in the mirror. I pushed her head down again and held her hair bunched in my hand. I leaned back and watched the mirror. She was moaning lightly and smiling. Smiling at me in the mirror. I grabbed her hips. She reached through her legs and very gently stroked my balls. The unaccustomed gentleness, at odds with everything else, made me climax quickly, and as I emptied into her she came too and my strength drained from me as though I was losing blood. I just avoided collapsing on top her as

I rolled to the side of the bed, tired and weak as death. The last sound I heard was her laughing.

I woke at 11.00 to the familiar sound of music and Yamilia singing. I wasn't hung over, the water from the night before had spared me that. Unfamiliar smells wafted into the bedroom. She was cooking. The smell of bacon reminded me that I was hungry. Breakfast was rare and usually accompanied with the accusation that I never made it. I washed quickly and approached the dining table next to the kitchen. The table was set with a clean white tablecloth adorned with flowers cut from the garden and plates, cutlery, coffee, bread and fruit. I approached cautiously and looked into the kitchen. She stood with her back to me at the sink in shorts and t-shirt, busy and still singing. I stood silently and watched, but after a few seconds she wiggled her bottom at me without turning round.

'Buenas dias, mi amor,' she said, 'como esta? Sentado por favor.'

She'd set a plate for herself – she didn't usually eat in the morning. She stood behind me, reached around and poured coffee. She stroked my shoulder as she moved away. Soon she was back with bacon, eggs, mushrooms and tomatoes. She sat down opposite and poured herself some water, began to eat.

'Eat, mi amor.'

We ate in silence for a while.

'Big surprise for me in the night,' she said.

She smiled her most beautiful of smiles and winked at me.

One hour of downright love is worth an age of dully living on.
Aphra Benn

THE BLUE HOUSE

The move came not long before I was due to leave the country again to renew my visa. Tony assured me it would be the last time, that from now there would be no need, he would take care of it. For a price. He had made the arrangements for the new house: lots of documents and signatures, witnessed solemnly in a lawyer's office in Guanabacoa. Yamilia thought she owned the house, although I was assured by Tony that she didn't. That wouldn't be wise. His name was on the deeds, although it would appear that someone else was living there. Would we tolerate the occasional company of Chuchi and his wife? She would cook if we liked and Chuchi would do odd jobs.

That seemed as solid arrangement as I would find. I doubted the house would ever truly be mine or that I would see any money from its sale. I knew that in effect I was buying a house for Tony, merely paying advance rent, but I already loved the house, imagined the fun to be had there, if not the domestic bliss. And it was $9000 dollars, nothing, I thought at the time. And, of course, Yamilia owning the house, no, that wouldn't have been wise.

I enjoyed life in the Blue House. At first old habits remained; we went out often, although there wasn't much to do in Guanabacoa and Havana was now a fairly long drive or taxi journey. Gradually, apart from weekends, we stopped going out and people came to us. It became a typical Cuban house with people coming and going day and night – constant noise, chatter and music – constant life. Even José was welcome – the single guest one night when Yamilia cooked, a peace offering of sorts – just me, Yamilia and José, drinking rum and watching baseball and talking. Strange how similar life had become to the life I'd left at home – drinking and watching sport on TV. Or maybe not so strange.

The next day we spent a lazy afternoon people-watching at La Catedral in Havana. A group of young, self-conscious, well-dressed young men made their slow way across the square. 'Italiano,' said Yamilia.

José nodded sagely.

'Gay,' he said.

Yamilia gave them her full attention.

'Si, gay,' she said sadly, shaking her head, 'ay, beautiful boys.'

She whispered in my ear, covered her mouth with her hand,

'Chris, Raul is gay.'

'Raul, mi medico?'

'No.'

She stroked her chin to indicate our bearded leader. José nodded conspiratorially.

'Hermano de Jefe,' she said, the brother of Fidel, and, looking around the square, she touched a finger to her lips.

We were pestered by a local nuisance. Unlike other, thankfully rare Cubans, who asked for money, she pestered and wouldn't be discouraged. After a few minutes Yamilia reached for her handbag and handed her a dollar. The woman, in a voluminous multi-coloured dress that she appeared to fill quite comfortably, accepted gracelessly and, in her own time, left our table. She wandered over to the other side of the square, then up a small side street and, still in view of the entire square, hitched up her dress, revealing a big, brown, pant-less arse and pissed up against the wall, standing, leaning back like a man; a long torrential gush.

'Ay,' said Yamilia, as she and José hid their faces behind their hands.

The woman, oblivious, wandered off to annoy tourists elsewhere.

As night drew in we went to the bar where I'd first been with Yamilia on our first night, two years before. It faced the street, its tables divided from the passing public by a small fence. No Cuban could get past that without the right company or money. Every night a girl, pretty and a bit overweight came to dance to the music. She stood outside the fence, dancing alone, oblivious to all but the music, throwing smiles at the musicians as though they were her personal friends. Or maybe just the music was her friend. It could have been sad, but it wasn't.

Tonight a new dancer appeared, a tiny man in dirty working clothes. I am not exaggerating when I say that he made Michael Jackson look clumsy and dull, and slowly he grabbed the attention of the whole bar, including the musicians, who began to play just for him. He performed there, in his own world, for perhaps twenty minutes, stopping when the band took a break. The entire bar stood for him, cheering loudly and clapping. He smiled and bowed modestly; one or two tourists offered him money. He shook his head and disappeared into the night.

Tony visited every day, a lordly presence, checking that everything was OK, that I'd been accepted as a neighbour and that no CDR members had reported us. One of his sisters, Silvia, lived a few doors away, a malevolent presence. Charming to my face, the dull hardness of her eyes was less welcoming. She tolerated Yamilia with a fixed smile of martyred superiority.

'Is she CDR?' I asked José.

'I don't know, maybe. She doesn't like me. I don't think she likes you; she doesn't want you in this house. Now you have paid the money she would like to see you go, take the house for herself.'

'But what about Tony?'

'Sure. Tony controls the family. He likes you. And he likes money. If you make him money he will look after you. If you have no money...'

He shrugged.

Silvia, tall, fiftyish, very white with white hair, carried herself as though she believed that, but for the revolution, she would have her rightful place among the aristocracy. She visited regularly when I had a fever, two or three times a day with home-made soup. Carrying the soup to the kitchen one day, she passed me as I watched baseball with

José. Tony was in the kitchen making coffee. I heard them talking and glanced in their direction. Silvia pointed at José, who had his back to them. She made a V of her right index and middle-finger and tapped them against her left upper arm. Whatever she meant, Tony dismissed it with impatience. After she'd gone I told José, asked him what she meant. He laughed.

'It's because I'm black,' he said, 'it's a sign some white Cubans make to each other. It means: he's black, he's trouble.'

Tony didn't like the arrangement I had with José in Santiago. He'd changed his opinion, emphasised how unreliable he thought José was, how although the business was going well now, José could be distracted at any moment, meet someone else, take my money and disappear. I disagreed. José was young and reckless, though probably less so than me, and I thought of him as good a friend as I'd find; he was smart and knew the streets, which Tony didn't. He stole small amounts, but never too much.

I decided to keep Tony happy and let him come up with an idea for another business. He did. It was exactly the same idea. Buy three cars, keep them in Tony's drive and rent them out. The only small difference was that they would be rented only to well-off Cubans. This was a neat touch and typical of Tony. He would have more control, the Cubans would know the game – they wouldn't pay so much – but it was safer. Nothing with José was ever quite safe.

I enthused about this as though it was the best, most original idea I had ever heard, giving Tony due credit for his business acumen. I didn't make much from it. The cars were not new or air-conditioned, but for Cuban families on a tour or visiting relatives – the smart cars were for foreign tourists. It was an income. I don't know how much Tony took, too much I'm sure, but as I didn't do anything apart from buy the cars I didn't complain. It was time for my visa. I chose Mexico City again because the journey was familiar and fast. I wanted to return as soon as possible – return home. That's how I felt; this was home, where I wanted to be.

Yamilia began to distrust Tony, whose innate distrust of her was no longer quite so well-hidden. She felt less secure in the house, watching suspiciously when I talked with him. Bizarrely, in her paranoia about the house, she formed an alliance with José, who had also begun to resent Tony, both of them childishly, possessively, criticising him for his growing influence over me. I didn't mind at all. It also meant José and Celia became frequent visitors.

We often visited a beach near Matanzas. José had discovered it, a beach for Cubans free of tourists, a small bay hidden from the road by forest. It was never crowded, used mainly by local people. There was a scruffy hut from which they served beer and rum, cooked anything you wanted, including freshly caught fish. The atmosphere was unstrained and relaxed. Celia was confident enough to talk to me without fear of Yamilia.

We watched as they brought an enormous fish ashore. It was an ugly thing, fat, about four feet long. They carried it to the restaurant on the beach. The owner said: 'Do you want us to cook it for you?' They cooked it and put it on our table with some salad. We ate what we could and gave the rest to some kids. As we sat eating Yamilia asked about the eyes: Were they good? Did they give you strength? José curled his lip, Celia turned away, I wasn't going to try. She speared an eye with her fork, put it in her mouth and crunched it, smiling; she did the same with the other one, all the time watching us, a light in her eyes that said: 'You know I'm badder than you are.'

We had stayed long after our usual time. I always drove back to Havana in daylight, but today it seemed none of us had any desire to leave. The sun was a fierce orange ball sitting on the horizon, its warmth already directed else-where, the silhouette of a lone pelican drifted heavily, lazily across the shallows, full of fish.

'Where do pelicans go to sleep?' I said.

Yamilia rolled her eyes. José and Celia just laughed. The downward movement of the sun was tangible, the day turning grey to dark blue and suddenly pitch black. After a few seconds of respectful, eerie silence, as if waiting a while to be sure the sun had really gone, the nocturnal cacophony clicked, buzzed and screeched into life in the woods behind us. We could hear the loud slaps of unseen people dealing with the emerging mosquitoes.

Yamilia shivered.

'If we light a fire the mosquitoes will stay away,' said José.

'We don't have any food or water,' I said. The hut was closed.

'Give me the car keys. I'll find a place.'

We stayed the night on the beach, sleeping for a few hours in our clothes for warmth, although it never became cold. After waking up with a swim we ate breakfast by the now open shack. For an entire day the four of us had lived in complete harmony – friends. There was no reason why it shouldn't stay that way, and I allowed myself to believe that it could. But this was the last truly peaceful day we would spend together.

Love is like war: easy to begin but very hard to stop.
H L Mencken

AMADO CALLS

The night before my flight I was alone in the house when the phone rang. A male voice said,

'Old man, this is not your house, it belong to me. My house, my woman.'

The line went dead. I told Yamilia when she returned from shopping. Feigned nonchalance failed to conceal the fear in her eyes. She walked to the kitchen and busied herself putting things away. Then she changed the subject. I called Tony. He was cool, dismissive of the call. I may have imagined the tension in his voice.

'Don't worry,' he said, 'I will deal with it.'

Deal with what?

I was back within forty-eight hours. Chuchi and Maria were alone in the house. They welcomed me as though I'd been away for a year. Yamilia was out. Maria fussed about me, gave me masses of food, tried to persuade me to sleep off the journey, although it was only a two-hour flight. Chuchi was just strange. Never exactly friendly before, he hovered around me, asked how I was, assured me that

Yamilia would be back soon, that everything had been absolutely fine in my absence.

Yamilia arrived soon afterwards on her bike, a bag full of shopping in the front basket. Food for the evening meal, rum and beer. She too fussed around me and invited Chuchi and Maria to stay for dinner. As we ate Yamilia showed me her front tooth.

'Look, Chris, I fall off my bike.'

She touched a broken tooth with a fingernail.

'I must go dentist. My smile!'

They chattered too fast of how Yamilia had hit a pothole and gone over the bars, chipping a front tooth and banging her head. Comico. Yamilia was so silly. She should look where she is going. Not so beautiful now, eh? Maybe the bang on her head would do some good. Maybe not so crazy now? I smiled with them. They kept my glass full all evening. Yamilia was attentive that night, taking nothing for herself, which was unusual. It didn't help me sleep though.

Yamilia and Maria went to Lucia's the next day. Lucia would speak to Raul, Raul would speak to someone and Yamilia would get her tooth fixed. Chuchi pottered around the house, smiling horribly at me whenever we met. When he offered to make me coffee I knew something was terribly wrong. I told him I was going out to buy cigarettes.

Silvia was sweeping her patio. She gave me her thin, joyless smile. A friend sat drinking coffee.

'Café, Chris?'

We sat at under a large umbrella, the air thick with malice. They waited. Silvia had no English, but her friend did, possibly why she was there. I considered leaving, accepting Yamilia's story, pretending that nothing had happened. The two women waited for their cue.

'What happened?'

Silvia sighed, as if regretting having to repeat such a tale. She spat rapid Spanish in small bursts at her friend, who translated. Two nights ago there had been a commotion. Banging on the door of my house and shouting. It was Amado. He shouted for Yamilia to come out. She shouted through the window, told him to leave, but he stayed, banging and shouting. The whole street could hear, they came out to watch. Yamilia stepped into the street. Amado shouted that this was his house, she was his woman. They couldn't hear what Yamilia said, she spoke quietly. He hit her on the side of the face. She stood with her hands on her hips. He hit her again and she fell down. He picked her up by her hair and threw her into the street and kicked her. Everybody saw this. It was disgraceful. Maria opened the door and shouted at Amado. He would have hit her too, but I called for the CDR. Maria took Yamilia back in the house. One of the CDR men stamped on Ricardo's foot and slapped his face. He got on his motorbike and drove away, making the people in the street jump out of the way.

'Chris, this is disgraceful. We cannot have this behaviour here. Everybody knows that woman will bring trouble. The CDR have been very tolerant of your parties, but you must be careful here, not draw attention to yourselves. These houses are respectable.'

'Amado,' I said, 'the son of Lazaro? Why did he come here?'

Silvia jerked her shoulders and looked away.

'Gracias por la café, Silvia.'

I called José and took a taxi to Havana. On the way I called Paul.

'So is this guy going to affect you, us?'

'It's a long story.'

'Hmm, why doesn't that surprise me?'

'I'd like him out of the way.'

'Have him killed.'

In Havana I gave José the story.

'You want to kill him?' said José.

'Can I? Would I get away with that?'

'No.'

The big difference between sex for money and sex for free is that sex for money usually costs a lot less.
Brendan Behan

AFTERMATH

Yamilia set the plates on the table under the mimosa tree. It was shady and cool in the yard; a breeze rustled the bougainvillea against the high walls. Guanabacoa was a noisy, rough town, but here on the patio the sound was muffled. There was rain in the air, still a few hours away. Yamilia ordered everybody from the house when Raul said I needed peace and quiet. She took advantage of the privacy and was wearing only a pair of my boxer shorts, though I had trouble appreciating it. I could barely move to eat my food. Everything ached. The light hurt my eyes. My fingers wouldn't work. A fly settled on the wound at the back of my head, I couldn't shake it off. Yamilia sprang at it and waved it away.

'Hijo de puta!'

She lightly stroked the area around the bald patch where Raul had shaved and stitched me up, carefully placed a sunhat there. She watched me eat. It was a slow, painful process but I was hungry. She nodded and smiled, if I wanted food I must be OK. She gave me an evil smirk. I groaned inwardly and hoped she was joking.

She cleared away the plates, singing in Spanish as she clattered about in the kitchen. I wondered idly if she'd break anything – it was a rare day that she didn't. She came to the door drying a plate, fixed her black eyes on me.

'You white, like a spirit.'

I'd lost a lot of blood through the head wound. She reeled off Raul's instructions, trying to rouse me, in precise English:

'Lots of sleep, lots of sugar and two tablets, three times every day. No smoking, lots of fruit, lots of water – and no rum.'

She vanished into the kitchen. She stopped singing, just the banging of pots and pans. She returned and sat down, her lips a tight line, a foot twitching. Angry now, angry because she wasn't happy, because something had happened that she didn't want to think about, something that would affect her life.

'You nearly die,' she said.

'Amado hurt you.'

'No importante.'

'It's important.'

I wanted to kill him or, more accurately, I wanted him to not be around anymore. My anger subsided, but I had to do *something*. Not wanting to end up in front of a firing squad and, truthfully, not having that much violence in me, I settled for breaking his nose with a kid's miniature baseball bat. It was worth it just for the look on his face. The second he opened his door, I hit him; flattened his nose, splattered his white shirt with red, spoiled his greasy good looks for a while. Easy. And dumb.

I didn't go home, but drove to Tony's house, where we used to stay. He was out so I waited, and helped myself to his rum. I got smugly, happily drunk and opened the door to someone I didn't know. A woman. Later she stamped on my hand. Amado and a couple of friends waited behind her. They stabbed and kicked me, hit me over the head with a hammer and left me bleeding on Tony's cool tiled floor. There I would have stayed but for Dingo. He created such a racket until the neighbours were forced to investigate. They found me in a spreading pool of my own blood. I woke up at Raul's house a couple of days later. They couldn't take me to hospital because the security police would have taken an interest. So Raul patched me up. Again. Muchas gracias, Dingo.

'He called me a maricon,' I said.

'Que?'

'Amado, at Tony's, before I went to sleep, while they kicked me. He called me a maricon, many times.

She was silent for a long time, eyes wide, eyebrows high on her forehead. Then she threw back her head and laughed. Her laughter changed everything – her, me, the atmosphere, the world. She found the funny side and was happy again. I failed to see the joke. She gave me a look that made men jealous of me at fifty paces.

'You? A maricon?' Gay.

'Si.'

'You no maricon, you fuck me every day.'

She collapsed into hysterics again. I suppose it was funny, but laughing hurt my ribs. She went to the kitchen. I heard her opening the fridge, crashing about, the clinking of glass and pouring. She returned with two large straight glasses filled to the brim with rum, soda and ice. She saw my surprise and shrugged.

'Your medicine. I put sugar in, and two tablets. I know you. No rum, you die.'

We touched glasses, 'Fidel.' I took a large swallow; it burned the cuts on my lips and mouth, then a few seconds later a wonderful calm. All was right with the world. The miracle of Cuban white rum. I took another sip. Somehow she got me to the bedroom, took the glass from me and put it on the floor.

'Slow down. Later.'

Later, the only sound in the room was the rise and fall of her breathing. The pain and solitary rage seeped out of me, as my blood had a few days before. Images of Amado, his green eyes as devoid of light as a reptile's, receded and my world contained only the rare, natural force of her. Her eyes clouded, her face grew soft and she slapped my face hard. She dug her nails into my chest, opening one of the cuts, which bled onto the sheet. I felt myself swell and burn painfully, and cried out as she did. And in those moments I was with her, inside the heat of her, as her sweat dripped onto my face and the smell of mariposa rose from her hair. And I was happy, in the only way I can be made happy, with a woman who understood that perfectly well.

I slept immediately. When I woke Yamilia was leaning against the doorframe, smoking a sorry looking joint. She wore my boxer shorts again, back to front this time. She still looked great. She glared at me, her eyes hard and dangerous. I asked for the joint. She ignored me.

'You no die,' she said.

It sounded like a threat; she'd punish me if I died.

'Not just yet.'

'No,' she shouted, 'You no die. I want baby.'

'OK'.

She puffed furiously on the joint, her eyes unfocussed, lost in her head, a look I knew well, best to keep her away from knives, anything she could throw or break. Then she changed, snapped out of it, threw the joint onto the patio. It sparked off one of the cats, who squeaked in protest, jumped, and ran off fast. She didn't notice. She came to the bed, seemed to see the open cut for the first time.

'Lo siento.' Sorry. She dropped some saliva over the cut, spread it with her tongue.

'Is good baby. Your eyes, your head, and this.' She pointed to my legs. She often did this. Once, as I completed a driving manoeuvre, she nodded her head in approval, said, 'Hmm, good coordination.' She was ticking off her genetic shopping list. Creating a beautiful child in her mind. She was quite open about it. There were plenty of faults too.

'You want my legs?'

'Me flaco,' she said, glaring angrily at her legs.

'Your legs are good.'

'Flaco,' she said, ending it. Skinny. 'You love me?'

'Siempre,' I said. Always.

She smiled.

'You want baby?'

'Sure,' I said, not sure at all. 'My blue eyes, tu negra corazon.'

'My black hat,' she said. Heart. As she flashed the eyes

189

and the teeth at me, I wondered again what I was doing here. The web of the black widow. She smiled happily, tried to stroke me into life again.

'Can we start tomorrow, Yamilia? I need to sleep.'

'Me too.' It was four in the afternoon.

She took three Diazepam from her bag and swallowed them. They can be bought over the counter for a penny each. She lay down next to me. I woke the next morning. I felt good, although I hadn't tried moving. She was still asleep beside me. A month later we were finished. And I'd started a war. Well, somebody had.

I do not cultivate the same tastes as tourists...
Che Guevara

PAUL RETURNS

Paul arrived for his second visit just as I had been passed fit again by Raul. He brought six detective novels with him. Disappointed by his lack of enthusiasm on the previous visit, we did our best to entertain him. He said he liked the house, although we'd yet to install a flushing toilet. On the first morning he blocked it with toilet paper and was mortified as Yamilia set to work with a plunger and buckets of water, showing him where the paper went and giving him instructions for future use. Our toilet flushed by filling a bucket to pour down the bowl, our shower was fed by three plastic containers, high above the patio. Efficient but basic. I wanted to impress Paul with my home, but a millionaire's son, used to five-star hotels, was hardly likely to be impressed with the amenities. Welcome to Cuba.

He seemed to have regained enthusiasm for the business, said we could charter tourists from England, and with the help of Rumbos, a tourist arm of the Cuban government, show them a good time here. Sell it with the hint of a Cuba the other tourists don't get to see. Set it up, pick the right employees, sit back, do very little – and get rich. It sounded great, easy, as ideas do when you're drunk and they remain dreams. Tony hadn't managed to arrange the meeting yet, but it would be set for next month, when Paul would return.

Apart from complaining about the rough and ready nature of most things Cuban, Paul remained indifferent to Havana. Where I saw magic, colour and character, he saw squalor and inefficiency. He couldn't adjust to Cuban attitudes to time and service. Our social life revolved around the handful of top hotels. I like the peso bars; Paul liked the Melia Cohiba. This only mattered when he was sober. Most of the time he was drunk and indifferent to what country he was in, let alone which bar or restaurant. And anyway, it was me and not him who wanted to live here. The purpose of the visit was to see if we could make money in Cuba.

Paul, surprisingly, struck up a friendship with Chuchi. They spent hours fiddling with my laptop, which I only used to keep a diary and watch DVDs. His booming voice and Chuchi's annoying whine accompanied many an afternoon otherwise occupied by TV baseball and music. Paul was determined to obtain internet access, available only at selected hotels. Even I, a confirmed Luddite, knew this would be impossible, but it didn't stop them trying. I liked Chuchi, but he annoyed me with his constant pottering and smug superiority. He performed the simplest task, like fitting an extension lead to the stereo, then fixed me with a supercilious grin, implying that without him these tasks would never be completed, the useless Englishman was too soft and lazy to work it out.

Our water came from three plastic tanks, high up on platforms at the back of the patio. Running water was available for two or three hours in the evening, when we filled the tanks. Chuchi liked to take over the task of filling them with a hosepipe attached to an outside tap. But I liked to do it too. We had a battle over who filled the tanks. He arrived every evening to find me there, contentedly filling the tanks myself. It relaxed me. I enjoyed it, but he spoilt my enjoyment by watching, arms folded, his expression one of pity because I wasn't doing the job properly, a job that a monkey could do. It was impossible to get it wrong. After he and Paul discovered their shared interest in technology, Chuchi expanded on my deficiencies,

'Paul very intelligent, you no.'

Maria was different. She was short, round and very hairy; hair on her face, arms and legs and, I presume, everywhere else. Yamilia pointed this out one day in Chuchi's presence:

'Ella es tu esposa, Chuchi, tiene que mucho gustar.'

This is the wife you chose, you must like them round and hairy. Whatever, Chuchi rarely took his eyes from Yamilia as she moved around the house. Maria was a great cook and cleaned constantly. I liked the way the bedlinen was always clean and fresh, without the chemical smell you often get in hotels. She washed it every day, working all day, every day: washing, cleaning, mopping, and cooking, usually with people and gossip and music to accompany her. I don't remember ever seeing an unclean room or house in Cuba. Daily cleaning was necessary – it was one chore Yamilia always did religiously, no matter where we were – to keep insects at bay. Crawling insects had no chance with the daily mopping and cleaning; I'd never seen a cockroach. Maria liked to rule the kitchen and I was happy to let her. Yamilia shadowed her though, occasionally doing something to help, but mainly gossiping. Maria didn't want any help. She didn't want anyone else in her kitchen. The strain showed on her face. I don't think she even liked Yamilia, but Yamilia was the lady of the house and she put up with it.

During Paul's second week I had a mild fever. On a bad day I stayed at home while Paul, José, Yamilia and Manolo went to the beach. In the evening I joined them around a TV game. I thought I could drink myself out of it. Paul said that they had bought cocaine and taken it to the beach. He fell asleep in the sun and now had lobster legs. Yamilia had said nothing about that to me. It was nothing, but it set off all the doubts of the previous months. Yamilia said she hadn't taken any, that she didn't like it, but I became jealous beyond reason. I shouted, accusing them all of assorted betrayals and deceits. They watched me in silence, which made me worse. I accused Paul of cheating me, José of stealing my money and Yamilia of everything I could think of. I paced shouting and swigging from a bottle of rum. My cheeks were burning. Then the ceiling receded before my eyes and my head hit the floor.

Yamilia woke me the next afternoon. A taxi waited to take me to Lucia's. I allowed myself to be dressed and taken to the taxi. I didn't stop my accusations as the taxi door closed. Another taxi waited for Paul, who was leaving. I wanted Yamilia to stay with me, but couldn't stop shouting at her. Paul's taxi followed to Villa Pan Americana. It pulled in behind us and Paul, Chuchi and José got out. Paul opened the door, leaned in and hugged me. He smiled and laughed, talked to me, an echoing jumble of words. I tried to push him away but was too weak. He kissed me on the cheek. They smiled as though they were admiring a new baby. My head boiled, a sound like radio static in my ears. Just fuck off, fuck off and then fuck off some more. Don't leave me here. What's so funny? Am I dying? The lights are too bright. I want to sleep, but I can't. And then they were gone and Yamilia and Lucia took me to the surgery.

I had pneumonia. Raul hunted down various medicines and drugs at other clinics and hospitals. The embargo gave the health service serious problems, making drugs common to us hard to find. Their expressions and hushed conversations worried me more than how I felt, which was just tired and hot or cold. I drifted in and out of sleep, oblivious of time. Yamilia came and went, sometimes staying the night. She was comfortable and welcome at Lucia's anyway.

After a week Raul declared me fit to go home under strict conditions. I was to stop smoking. Alcohol was banned until I was fit again. I felt refreshed by the sleep and, for a time, didn't want to drink or smoke anyway. I read and reread my books, watched TV, DVDs and slept. Yamilia, always good when I was ill, fussed around me while Maria did the work. I slowly felt awake and alive, as if waking from months of sleep, slightly baffled as to how I'd got here.

Raul or Lucia or both visited every day. Raul gave me something that made me throw up regularly, to get the phlegm off of my chest. Very slowly I slid into a drowsy contentment, an appreciation of what I had, a different outlook, a sober outlook. Tony, concerned at first – a dead Englishman would be awkward – was happy to have a calm house to administer, no problems for him to smooth over. The calmness was catching, the house lost its manic energy, was quieter, more at peace with itself. I heard nothing of Amado or Lazaro, which may or may not have been due to Tony. He made an appointment with Rumbos for the next month when Paul returned. Plenty of time to prepare.

Luck is believing you're lucky.
Tennessee Williams

Matanzas

I parked the jeep at the centre of the bridge, the longest and highest in Cuba. It was a tourist spot so there was room on both sides of the road. Far below, and south as far as I could see, was tropical forest. To the north behind me a clear view of the sea, a few hundred yards away. For the same reason that it was a tourist spot, the bridge also posed a security risk. Approaching, I passed the usual Lada up on the slope, two bored policemen inside, waiting for nothing to happen.

I leaned against the railings and looked at the forest below, vultures flew *under* the bridge. I like vultures, without them the smell of death would be everywhere. They don't bother anyone, unless you happen to be dead, and they clean everything up before lumbering off to digest it – ugly great birds providing a valuable social service and minding their own business. On the slope a motorcycle cop had parked next to the Lada, was talking through the window. They were about two hundred yards away. I knew I should leave, find another place or try another day, but I'd made up my mind. I'd had the box with me for far too long. Yamilia had finally lost patience that morning when a priest of Santeria came to bless the new house. 'Get it out of here,' she shouted. We argued for a while, but she was right; I understood why it spooked her. I left with the box, bought a cheap spade in Guanabacoa and drove to Havana. I parked and walked to Plaza Armas. I thought I could put them in the ground there among the plants, maybe sprinkle some seeds, or come back later with a sapling. There were worse places to rest, at the heart of socialism's last stand, pretty girls passing by all day and night.

One look told me it was impossible: too many people, police on every corner. How would I explain it? It couldn't be explained. So I drove to the bridge, fifty miles from Havana, ten miles before Matanzas, and, regardless of the police on the hill, I was going no further. I watched them. They weren't using binoculars; they were just talking. I wasn't doing anything wrong. What could they do? I took the box from the jeep and put it down on the road. I realised that in fifteen years I'd never even opened it. It was still sealed with brown tape. I opened it and took out the plastic urn, unscrewed the top and shook the ashes into the strong wind. For a few seconds they had shape, like a plume of smoke, and then they scattered and disappeared. I dropped the urn back in the box. There are still worse places to be, I thought.

I tried for a few moments' meditation, soon interrupted by the motorcycle cop riding slowly across the bridge. I glanced as he passed: a snapshot of gleaming chrome, blue uniform, black helmet, reflective sunglasses and knee high, shiny black leather boots. He stared back and rode over the bridge and parked on the opposite slope. I went back to the view. I was certain now that at some stage they would speak to me. The cardboard box still lay at my feet. They had seen me throw something. If they asked what was in the box, what could I say? Not the truth. I decided to risk getting rid of it. I picked it up and dropped it through the railings, watched it take forever to float to the forest below. They were with me in seconds. What are you doing here? What have you just thrown? Who are you? Where are you from? I said I'd been eating my lunch, had thrown the empty box away. Not very good, but what could they do? They could do plenty as it turned out.

They leaned over the railings to see what I'd thrown. They took my wallet and passport. I tried to explain. The motorcycle cop ignored me, lost in his own self-importance. He walked to his bike and spoke into the radio. This was going to get silly. I knew it would get worse because I wasn't behaving in a confident manner. I was hiding something and I couldn't come up with anything that made much sense. I couldn't tell them the truth; they would never believe me. I didn't want to tell anyone the truth anyway.

They told me to drive the jeep to the slope where I'd first passed them. Motorcycle Man led the way a few feet in front of me. They indicated that I should wait in the jeep. The two cops went back to their car; Motorcycle Man kicked up dust and sped to the other side of the bridge. The two in the car were no longer taking this seriously. Maybe they decided that whatever I was up to, it wasn't criminal, or maybe they just didn't care. Their job was done for now. We were waiting for reinforcements. I hoped to be able to talk to them and get out of there.

While waiting I played music in the jeep, a compilation of all sorts of stuff. They watched from their car, then came over and asked questions about the music. When the security people arrived an hour later we were chatting normally, as though I didn't really have to be there. They arrived in several cars, not Ladas now, but sleek new models. Motorcycle Man, his lights on full beam, led them across the bridge. I was beginning to hate him.

They were serious people, some uniforms, mostly plain clothes, efficient and energetic. They parked on both sides of the road and spoke briefly to the two cops. I picked out the man in charge who was dispatching people to check the bridge. They couldn't get down to the forest, but they checked the road, leaned over to look at the supporting stanchions, scrambled down the banks to see underneath. This was so silly. It was Motorcycle Man: the box floated in the wind. What the hell did he think it was? I realised that the two from the Lada knew this, but Motorcycle Man was having his day, and he'd called in the report. Whatever really happened didn't matter anymore. The new people had to deal with what he'd told them.

I stayed in my jeep watching them, composing my face into an expression of bewildered, injured innocence. The boss stopped telling his men what to do and stood by his car watching. This was a serious security call, his responsibility; he was ensuring he had everything covered. Traffic was being slowed by the parked cars. I watched as he considered whether to stop it during the check. He didn't, a good sign. Then he stared at Motorcycle Man, who was telling anyone who would listen how he'd saved the day. His eyebrows rose, he pursed his lips and I saw, or hoped

I saw, a slight, dismissive shake of the head. Even better. Then he looked over at me and I felt a stab of panic.

He walked to the jeep and ordered me out, looked me over without speaking. He was short, powerfully built, well dressed and handsome with piercing green eyes. He shouted an order and two men began to search the jeep. He spoke to Motorcycle Man, then to the two Lada cops, who he asked for my wallet. They came out of the jeep with some cassettes, an address book, cigarettes, lighter, condoms, a novel, a Cuban published history of the country, a map of Cuba, a pair of Yamilia's sunglasses, one of her tops from behind the seat, and the spade. He looked at the spade and then at me, told me to get in the jeep. He got in beside me and closed the door. The music was still playing. He had my wallet, passport, address book and the map.

He opened the passport and confirmed my details, then went through it page by page. I tried to appear confident. I wasn't worried about the box and the bridge; surely, eventually they would realise that was nonsense. I worried about what they would find out while they found that out. I owned a house in Guanabacoa. That was illegal. It was illegal to even stay in an unregistered house; that was how the security police knew where everyone was. Yamilia's papers weren't legal. My friends and visitors were up to all sorts of stuff that would interest these people. I imagined the house now. Yamilia was there, perhaps the Santeria guy too, probably Chuchi and Maria. And the deeds to the house – Tony had those. I imagined everyone I knew being arrested, the house confiscated and me deported. I'd been lucky up to now, and protected up to a point. My whole life in Cuba could collapse because of this. I was very, very uneasy and had no idea what to tell them, just a very vague plan: get them to like me, appear relaxed and play it by ear. Brilliant.

'You have visited Cuba eleven times in three years, Mr Hilton.'

'I love Cuba.'

No reaction, just a hard stare.

'You have been here for many months. In that time you have made three visits to Mexico and one to Panama. Where have you been staying? What have you been doing?'

'I've stayed in lots of places, all over the country. I want to start a travel business with Rumbos. I've been travelling, looking at hotels and planning itineraries.'

That made him think. Rumbos were the tourist arm of the government, if you wanted to work in tourism you had to meet with them. I'd met with Rumbos once. I hoped they remembered. He went back to the passport and looked through the other stamps. The USA, three times, just before I started visiting Cuba, the most recent visit lasting five weeks. I liked the variety of stamps in my passport. Now, as he studied them, I wished they weren't there.

'You spent much time in the United States in 1997 and 1998.'

'I have friends there.'

'Then you began to visit Cuba.'

'After one visit I didn't want to go anywhere else.'

He lowered his head, studied me over his sunglasses. He sighed with a big movement of his shoulders and, still holding my open passport, turned to look out of the passenger window. He took off his sunglasses and tapped them to the music. The tape would keep repeating until someone turned it off. The searchers were all back, milling around. There was nothing to find.

'Where are you staying?'

'In Guanabacoa.'

'Where in Guanabacoa?'

'I stay at a house there.'

'What is the address?'

'I don't know the address.'

He gave me a weary look.

'You don't know your address?'

'No.'

It was true. I knew where I lived, but I didn't know the name of the street. It was an old colonial house with a big, blue arched door. I could find it easily, but I had no idea of the address.

'You should have a card with the owner's details. All government guesthouses are registered. You are staying at a registered house?'

'I don't know.'

'It is illegal to stay at an unregistered house. You could be deported.'

I knew that.

He sighed, tapped his glasses a little faster and looked over at Motorcycle Man. Again, I sensed mistrust, that he wondered if this traffic cop was as stupid as he looked, was wasting his time. It was enough for me to decide to play it that way: The loveable rogue who was not really up to anything bad enough to concern them.

'OK. Mr Hilton. We have a problem with terrorism in this country, particularly from the USA. You have been reported as having a similar appearance to someone we have been looking for. I don't know what you were doing here. We have to check everything. You will be taken to Matanzas police station and questioned. Some people will look over your vehicle.' He'd had enough. He called a colleague by name, Sanchez. He got out of the jeep, spoke to him and handed him my stuff, then walked to his car without a backward glance. Sanchez got in. He smiled pleasantly.

'You drive,' he said.

I drove the ten miles to Matanzas. Motorcycle Man led the way, lights on full beam. As we entered Matanzas he waved at people he knew, the conquering hero. I tried to talk to Sanchez. He said his name was Ramon. On the journey I tried to mock Motorcycle Man. 'Arrogante,' I said, pointing at his back. He turned to me, smiled his contented smile and asked for a cigarette. I parked in the yard of Matanzas Police Station. I knew the area. I'd been here before as a tourist, a rough place, good fun, but not one of the safest places in Cuba. Motorcycle Man, his duty done, was about to leave. I felt a sudden surge of hatred, got out of the jeep and headed towards him. Ramon walked slowly to the door of the police station, unconcerned. I got to within a few yards of his bike when he gunned it and, without acknowledging my existence, sped off, screeching tyres spraying dust in my face. I watched him go. Ramon stood at the entrance watching. He smiled and beckoned me in.

He had a big office, important man. He took his time, found some notepaper, a pen, and sat down opposite me. He started with my address. I didn't know. He smiled and wrote something down. Occasionally he spoke to a female assistant who entered information into a computer. Periodically, she fed him information back. They spoke rapid Cuban Spanish. I couldn't understand much of what was said, just odd words and phrases, names of hotels, dates and places I'd visited. I wanted to tailor my story to what they knew. He spread some of my stuff over his desk: my passport, address book and a tiny leather diary. He studied them. He studied them for a long time, stopped, smiled at me, and studied them all again.

'You don't know where you live?'

'I know where I live. I don't know the address.'

A charming smile. I thought: All he needs to do is ask me to take him there. To drive there now, an hour's drive. And I'm fucked. We're all fucked. He was looking through my passport, pausing now and then to smile at me. He asked me a question that I didn't understand. He tried another way. I still didn't understand. Hopeless.

'I will get an interpreter,' he said. 'We can't talk.'

He stood up.

'I'm going to eat,' he said. 'Come back here in one hour.'

'What shall I do?'

He shrugged.

'Do what you like.'

I went outside. I was hungry, tired and pissed off. And desperate for a cigarette. I hadn't smoked for over a month. Traffic was heavy and constant. I felt nauseous. I fetched a pack of duty-free cigarettes fom the jeep. As I sat on the steps smoking, a man of about sixty approached me, smiling. Handsome with white hair, tall and fit looking, nimble. He sat next to me on the steps.

'Is that a Benson and Hedges?'

'Yes.'

'Can I have one?'

'Sure.'

'My name is Noberto. Noberto Castro.'

'Castro?'

He shrugged off my surprise.

'Here it is like Smith in England. It's nothing. I am your interpreter. I live down the street here; they always call me when an English person is in trouble. So, you are a terrorist?'

'Do I look like a terrorist?'

He didn't reply immediately. His pale blue eyes studied me as he smoked his cigarette.

'No, you do not look like a terrorist. Something else, maybe, but not a terrorist. Why do they think you are?'

I told him.

'I see,' he said, 'so there is no problem. Just tell them the truth. People get themselves in trouble when they lie; these people check everything.'

'I was afraid of that.'

'Ah.'

'Where are you from in England?'

'Near London,' I said.

My stock answer.

'Where near London? Oxford? Essex? Kent? Canterbury? I know England. France, too. Fine countries. I lived there when I was younger. But this is Cuba. You may not be a terrorist, but I'm afraid you may have to go through some shit before they realise that, my friend.'

Ramon returned from his lunch. We went through the

same questions again as Noberto translated. Ramon smiled a lot and told me several times that I could be deported. He was interested in the tiny address book. It was full of phone numbers given to me in times and places that I couldn't remember, by people I couldn't remember.

'What are these numbers?'

I stared at the book. He turned it around for me. I studied the page for a few seconds, gave the appearance of deep thought. I shrugged.

'Chicas, I think.'

Ramon smiled and winked, Noberto smiled, I smiled – a communal smile – all boys together here. He put the book down, leaned back in his chair, and stretched with his hands behind his head.

'Your vehicle will have to be searched. I have made the necessary telephone calls.'

'What do I do?' I said.

'You wait. We can find you.'

We went to a bar close by. I bought us both a meal and some beers. I still hated beer, but was making a big effort to follow Raul's fitness regime.

'So what are you doing in Cuba, my friend? How long have you been here?'

'Nearly a year. I'm trying to start a tourism business.'

'Tourism. That's good. You must give me a job. I can translate for you. Tourism, that's where the money is. Remember me, my friend, when you start your business.'

'I will.'

'So. Do you have a woman here? Cuban women are the best in the world.'

'I know. Yes, I'm with a woman.'

'What is her name?'

'Yamilia.'

'Yamilia. A nice name. A good woman?'

I managed to keep a straight face.

'Yes. She's a good woman.'

'When will they come to search my car?'

'I don't know. This is Cuba. It could be a long time, my friend.'

'Why haven't they put me in a cell?'

'They will. This is all part of their games. Be very careful what you say.'

I decided to trust him. I didn't have much choice. They were clever enough to plant him on me, wait for me to drop myself in it, although I didn't sense that in him. And I clung to the hope that they didn't really care about me, that as long as I was polite and didn't offend them they would let me go. Once they confirmed I wasn't a terrorist. There was a public phone on the wall close to our table. It was probably listened to at least some of the time. I didn't see too many other choices.

'Can you call someone for me?'

'Of course. Who do you want me to call?'

'Can I talk freely to you?'

He was offended.

'Of course you can. The second I saw you I knew you were not a bad man. Fucking police. Don't worry. I only translate. I don't tell them anything.'

I told him all about the house in Guanabacoa. About Tony. I asked him to call the house. If Yamilia answered he was to ask for Chuchi. Tell Chuchi what had happened.

Tell him to call Tony. I watched him phone. Chuchi answered. Noberto spoke to him as though he'd known him all his life. Cuba was like that. They were all in this together. He put the phone down. He'd enjoyed himself.

'Chuchi will go to Tony and tell him. He doesn't want to talk on Tony's phone. Who is Tony?'

I told him. Said that I thought he had some influence, might be able to speed this up. He looked doubtful.

'I hope so, my friend. I hope so.'

We had time to spare, no sign of the inquisition. Norberto took me to his house, a spacious white villa in a row of spacious villas. I sat in his kitchen at a large hardwood dining table while he made coffee. Piles of old copies of *Granma* lined one wall, stacked in piles, yellowed and curling at the edges; copies too of *Le Figaro* and the *New York Times* – inflammatory stuff. Norberto's son arrived, thirtyish and overweight; at his father's request he gave me a limp sweaty palm to shake. He was sent to buy sugar but did not return. The house had a sad deserted feel, I didn't sense a woman's presence, nor did I think there had been one for many years. Then the phone rang. My inquisitors were on their way. We had only waited an hour.

Ramon waited in front of the station. Two minutes later they arrived in two cars, screeched to a halt in front of us. A van pulled in behind them. Six people got out, all armed. I had the impression they'd been disturbed from something important. A game of pool, perhaps. A dog handler released two Alsatians from the van. The men spoke to Ramon who beckoned to me. We all walked round the back of the station to where my jeep was parked among a row of other cars. They stood together with Ramon and Norberto. All casually dressed, mostly jeans, shirts and moustaches. One of them spoke to Ramon, who spoke to Noberto, who spoke to me.

'You must reverse your jeep to the centre of the car park.'

I reversed the jeep and got out.

'Now open the side doors and the back door. Leave them open.'

I opened the doors.

'Now stand away from the jeep on the other side. Don't come towards us.'

I did as I was told.

The handler let his dogs loose. They leapt enthusiastically into the jeep and sniffed everywhere. They sniffed the tyres; one crawled underneath and sniffed there. After a couple of minutes they began to whine impatiently. I knew what they were saying.

'There's nothing here. We're wasting our time.'

I was so fascinated by the dogs, so entertained, that I didn't notice the others. I turned to see six of them, guns drawn, straight-armed, Hollywood style, all pointing at me. I tried not to laugh, looked over at Norberto. He winked at me. The dogs were fed up. Their handler instructed them to repeat the process. They yelped in protest, but went through the motions, whining all the time: 'There's nothing here. Waste of time.' They gave up, barked in unison at their handler. He spoke to the others.

'Nada.'

In a moment they holstered their guns, muttered to each other, got in their cars and sped off, leaving me,

Ramon and Norberto alone in the car park. Ramon came towards me. Norberto translated.

'Mr Hilton. We owe you an apology. We have a problem with terrorism in our country. You were mistaken for someone we have been looking for.'

I stopped him, shook his hand.

'Forget it. I understand that you have to be careful. Thank you for your polite treatment. Can I go now?'

He said I could. His eyes told me that he knew I was returning to something distinctly illegal involving Cuban citizens. He didn't care, nor did the others – they had more important things to do. They'd ignored all the peripheral stuff. I was free. Ramon smiled his contented smile and walked away. I got into my jeep.

'Thank you, Norberto. Please take some money. I'm very grateful for all your help.'

'I don't want your money. Do you have more Benson and Hedges? I'll have those. Just give me a job when you start your business. I'm glad it worked out well for you. Your friend Tony. He must have some important friends.'

'Yes. I think he must.'

'Let me give you some advice. You have been lucky today, but don't underestimate people like Sanchez. He will smile at you as he locks you away. Don't forget, we learnt security from the Russians. We are not as slow as we seem. Be careful, my friend.'

I stopped at the first shop and bought a bottle of rum, my first in weeks. Driving back I smoked, drank and sang along with the music. I couldn't figure out what sort of day I'd had. I thought about my father. Had I done the right thing? Had what had happened been lucky or un-

lucky? How should I feel about it? Had I shown him respect, throwing his ashes off a road bridge in Cuba? He
would have settled for Upton Park. I didn't know. I just
knew I was happy and getting happier. I decided that I'd
had a good day, a little adventure and he'd looked after me.
That would do. I relaxed, took another swig of rum and
sang along to the music.

Que le pasa a esa mujer?: What's going on with that woman?
Juan Almeida Bosque, song title

CRY OUT IN YOUR SADNESS

Yamilia refused to accept what happened in Matanzas. She insisted that it was a made-up story; that I'd been with José and other women. Tony spoke to her. He told her that he'd spoken to the police in Matanzas who had confirmed my arrest, and to some friends in security who had speeded things up. She accused him of collaborating with us, the first time she'd been anything but polite to Tony. I offered her Noberto's phone number which she refused to call, saying that I could easily set someone up to speak to her. We waited for her to calm down. She didn't. She didn't let up at all, dragging whoever else happened to be in the house into the argument.

Her tantrums drove me from the house and I began meeting José in Havana, fuelling her accusations. We visited Aledmis, a friend of José, his flat an attic atop an apparently neglected or condemned tenement. Five flights of dusty stairs, creaking and dangerous, took us to the top of what remained of the building. Concrete and plaster dust floated in the sunlight. If the house was no longer solid, the loft was spacious and clean, partitioned off with curtains in bright greens, yellows and reds, interspersed with cushions, rescued furniture and a mattress. Some of the furniture he made himself from scraps. His water and electricity were filched from neighbours with creative plumbing and wiring.

They settled into a game of chess. Aledmis put the afternoon's baseball on for me by touching two wires together. A strangely sculpted antenna provided reception, put together with metal rods, coat hangers and wire. The aerial barely protruded lest snoopers enquire as to why a deserted property should require one. A DVD provided pirated films, big business in Cuba. I wondered why I hadn't been here before. I'd met Aledmis before briefly. He was polite, but cool. Perhaps he disapproved of me.

Aledmis gave about a third of his concentration to the chess while beating José several times. José, smarting from his humiliation at chess, began to bait me about Yamilia, a familiar argument. I argued that, contrary to popular belief, she was intelligent. What I meant, and still believe, is that she possessed an innate wisdom, that saw through bullshit, that she could sometimes encapsulate in Spanish, English or French, without prior thought, complex ideas and wonderful humour. But this was too fine a point to argue here, or at any time. Neither my Spanish nor José's English could handle it. The only person who would understand was Manolo and he hated her too much to be objective.

'Your woman is not intelligent,' said Aledmis with surprising force. 'The opportunities you have given her, she could have done so much. She could have learned a skill, educated herself and bought a house that would have been useful to you both, that could have been rented. She could have learned to drive, so many things, yet all she did was drive you crazy.'

He lay back again, conversation over and, it seemed, our company no longer required. As we walked along Obispo José was silent. He didn't need to speak; his expression spoke for him. It said:

'I told you so.'

Yamilia disappeared for two days. I didn't miss her. Nobody did; she had become an irritant to everybody, mocking and persistent with her indignation at something that clearly hadn't happened. I wondered if this was paranoid jealousy or if something else was happening, if outside pressures were affecting her. She'd also created an excuse to hate José again. I enjoyed the strange peace of the house, and realised how, even before this, Yamilia had put everyone on edge with her unpredictability. I began to think of Paul's next visit, our appointment with Rumbos. I read books, went shopping, smiled at girls in the street. I sensed a different life.

I had arranged to meet José and Celia at the Latin American stadium for the baseball. As I was preparing to leave Yamilia arrived in a taxi; she smiled and kissed everyone in the house, oblivious to the baffled stares.

'Where you go?' she said.

'To the baseball.'

'Who is playing?'

'Industriales and Pinar del Rio. I'm meeting José and Celia there.'

'I will come too.'

I held the taxi.

She was bright and happy at the game. We ate nuts, drank rum and enjoyed ourselves. I slipped right back into it, forgetting what had gone before. When she was happy, I was happy. When Yamilia wasn't looking, José shook his head, raised his eyebrows and chuckled at what he considered her performance.

'You are a crazy man,' he whispered to me.

Even Celia was at ease, such was Yamilia's cheerfulness. She invited them both back to the house. We watched a movie, drank some more and stayed up talking until late.

In the morning Yamilia wanted to go to the beach. Not one of the local beaches, but the one near Matanzas, where we had stayed the night once. We did the same things, but the atmosphere was vaguely tense and Yamilia drank too much. As I drove home she fell asleep, her head lolling from side to side in the front seat. We took it in turns to support her head, so loose that it seemed as though her neck might break. I was tired and wanted a drink or two to complete the journey. We stopped at a little roadside bar in the middle of nowhere. A surly barman gave as a bottle. Two old men sat at one of the tables. Yamilia slept on in the jeep. We drank and talked to the accompaniment of cicadas and the noise of passing traffic.

A door slammed. Yamilia stood looking around, blinking. She looked at the passing traffic and down the steps at the bar, the old men and us. Then she walked to the bar and ordered a beer.

'Ay por dios,' said José: 'Oh my God.'

Something in her voice. Celia shrank as Yamilia sat down opposite me, next to José.

'You want drink more?'

'I was tired, Yamilia, you were asleep.'

'You and your friend, you want drink more?' She turned to José, 'You want this man drink too much?'

She jerked her head at me. José said nothing. She turned to the barman, shouted something fast in Spanish. He ambled slowly to our table and put another beer in front of her. She laughed and said in English,

'Something wrong with your legs?'

He looked at her and then at me. His expression said: Are you going to do something about her? She shouted something at the two old men. They stared back at her without expression. She looked over her shoulder at the barman who was lazily cleaning a glass and watching her. Something in his manner upset her. She leapt from her chair, knocking it over and moved towards the bar. I couldn't understand what she was saying. She leaned on the bar, stuck out her ass at the rest of us. She asked him questions, which he ignored, cleaning glasses and staring at a space above her head. She answered for him, shrugging her shoulders, staring into his face. His blank eyes met mine. Are you going to do something? She gave up and walked unsteadily back to the table. She noticed the two old men again. She spread her arms:

'Ay, hombres viejo. Como esta? How are you?'

She sat back next to José, nodding slowly at me.

'Chris,' she said, 'my husband. You stop to drink more with your friend José. He is your good friend. José the knife man.'

She thumped José on the arm.

'José. You friend of my husband. You good man José. My husband think you are good man.'

She turned to Celia.

'You, you fuck my husband?'

She slammed her beer on the table. It frothed and spilled over her hand. Her head drooped forward and, for a moment, I thought we might be able to pick her up, carry her to the car and take her home. Then she looked up at me, eyes wild; she pushed back her chair, nearly fell over it and staggered to the old men's table. She spoke rapid fire Spanish at them, laughing at her own jokes. They stared back impassively, waiting to see what she would do next. She staggered into the next table, kicked a chair out of her way. They had metal bases and it must have hurt, but either she didn't feel it or chose not to show any pain. But she *was* showing her pain. She turned and stared at our table.

'Me no crazy,' she said, and, pointing shakily, '*you* crazy.'

She screamed at us. She kicked tables and chairs. She broke glasses and bottles. The barman and the two old Cubans didn't say anything. They hadn't been so entertained in ages. But they wondered why I didn't just shut her up. José wished he could, but he couldn't, because of me. And she knew that. She knew I wouldn't and she knew he couldn't, and she screamed out her hard life and her determined enjoyment of it. She took it out on us and I let her because I hoped she would be happy again the next day. And she knew I knew her. And she thought I would love her despite of it. The most honest, ballsy, don't give a shit person I've ever met, and she thought I would love her forever. And right now I did love her. I didn't care what José thought of my machismo or what the barman and the two old men thought of my ability to control my woman. I loved her more than ever. But I knew that we were finished.

The memory of you emerges from the night around me.
Pablo Neruda

BREAKING UP

Many of the problems with Yamilia stemmed from malentendidos, misunderstandings. Taking our faults into account, the weight of opinion against her, the age difference, everything, I still think we could have made it. But misunderstandings happen often enough with people of the same nationality. Add the language problem, a woman of gale force temperament and a middle-aged dreamer sliding into alcoholism and the potential is limitless.

She stayed for a few days, quiet and subdued, the memory of her performance at the bar hanging heavy over everything. We didn't smile or laugh, couldn't smile or laugh, skirting each other like two wary animals forced to stay in the same cage. One night she asked to eat at the Nacional, maybe for old times' sake. She was sulky during the meal. I was no better; conversation between us had dried up; we had everything and nothing to say. Still, she seemed in no hurry to leave, pouring frequent measures from our bottle.

'I want to fly,' she said.

'Fly? Fly where?'

'Fly with you, any place.'

She'd had enough of Havana. Enough of the battles she had to fight. And she wanted me to take her away from all that. Surely if I loved her I'd do that? I didn't want to leave Havana. Where would I take her? England? And whoever might be waiting for me there, wanting a quiet word? She waited for the answer that didn't come, drained her glass and rose to leave. The evening was over. Maybe that was when she decided to give up the struggle, fall on one side or the other.

That weekend I walked into the house to find Yamilia on the patio with some girlfriends I hadn't seen before. She didn't acknowledge my presence or introduce me. We passed a few times as we moved around the house. She gave me a look I'd seen so many others receive, scornful, an unpleasant light in her eyes. There was nothing I could say or do, nothing she would understand. This wasn't like other times, other rows, something was ending here.

More new friends appeared at the house. She stayed away for a couple of nights. Two hundred dollars disappeared from my wallet. I spent the time she was away with Manolo. He didn't attempt to disguise his dislike for Yamilia, partly, I knew, because the feeling was mutual.

'This is the beginning,' he said, 'she is making her move. They will be here soon to take everything.'

He took me to see some of his friends. One lived in a small palace, marble floors, antique and modern furniture mixed, expensive art and a large pool. Where did money like that come from? I didn't ask. We got drunk and talked about Yamilia. The friend's wife said,

'She is losing a good man.'

Right.

Manolo fed the insecurities that had never really died.

'She has been setting you up. Now she is back with Lazaro and Amado. They want the house. Amado wants his woman. They will come. You must speak to Tony. You can't deal with this.'

'Why have they waited so long? They could have done this anytime.'

'Because she didn't leave you. They need her on their side. She might have married you. That would have been a problem.'

'Why would that have been a problem?'

'She'd have the power. They would be out.'

'That doesn't make sense.'

He shrugged,

'Why should it? She's crazy.'

Yamilia returned one afternoon while I was watching football with José and Manolo. They both left. She sat in the other armchair and watched the game, drank a few beers. We talked a bit about nothing. It got late, she stood up, stretched and yawned. She stroked my neck as she passed behind my chair on her way to the bedroom. I was tired, but waited until she was asleep. As I settled down she put her arm round me. I jumped at her touch, not wanting it. I got out of bed and went back to the living room, sat down and lit a cigarette. After a minute she followed, and lit a cigarette too. She watched me in silence. I couldn't look at her. I looked straight ahead and finished my cigarette. Then I got up and went to a drawer and took out two diazepam. I swallowed one and offered the other to her. She looked up at me and we held each other's gaze for a few seconds, then she took the tablet from my hand and swallowed it. I let her go first. When I followed later she appeared to be asleep. I got into bed and lay down with my back to her.

I woke late the next day. Yamilia had gone. Maria gave me breakfast, let me finish my coffee and beckoned me to the living room. She pointed. Yamilia had taken the DVD player. Chuchi stood in the background, arms folded, nodding stupidly. I checked my wallet. There hadn't been much there but she'd taken what there was. I called Tony.

Tony asked for a glass of rum and a cigarette. He told Manolo to ask me if I agreed with his plan. José and Chuchi were there too. We had two cars, he said. We were to move all my stuff now. He suggested we take it to his other house, where I would stay. I said I wanted to go to Villa Pan Americana and Rosa. They would not expect me to be there. I had friends there and it was easier for José to reach. Raul and Lucia were neighbours. He was mildly offended but said OK. Later he, Manolo and Chuchi would return to chain and padlock the house. Don't worry, Chris, he said, if they want to fight we will fight them. It had the feeling of a military briefing. Everybody was a little pumped up and excited.

We moved all my stuff in one trip. Rosa welcomed me with an 'I told you so' attitude she couldn't restrain. The others went off to secure the house, Rosa left for her alternative accommodation, leaving me and José and a bottle of Silver Dry. We finished the bottle and then José left too. I said he could stay, but Celia was expecting him. I wanted more rum but only to knock me out, then decided against it. I trudged to the bedroom I'd shared for four months with Yamilia. It seemed ugly and desolate. I tossed and turned for an hour, then got up and tried to read. I couldn't concentrate. It was early morning in England, so I phoned Paul.

'When you arrive in three weeks you'll be staying at a different address.'

'Again? What have you been up to now?'

I told him the story.

'OK, doesn't change anything.'

But it did. It changed everything.

If this is dying, I don't think much of it.
Lytton Strachey, last words

TROUBLE

The Blue House was locked. Chains and padlocks secured its arched doors. People were looking for me, including Yamilia. Old friends stopped me and asked after Yamilia. 'Finito,' I'd say. They'd say: 'Sorry, you were a good couple,' or 'You looked happy.' It didn't help.

Lucia set up a meeting with Yamilia in her surgery. She wanted us back together. José was angry, but didn't try to stop me. Tony would be furious if he found out. Rosa wasn't pleased either. She was exasperated with me when she heard about the meeting.

'Chris, you have quality, this women is no good for you. She is crazy.' She pointed at her head to emphasise the extent of Yamilia's madness.

'Forget her. Make a life for yourself. Find a good woman. There are a thousand women here who would make you happy. She is bad. She will pull you down. I will marry you. You will be legal. You can live here and fuck who you like.'

Jose was still laughing at her brazenness as we left.

'Do you think she's right? Maybe I should marry her.'

'No,' he said, shaking his head. 'Do not believe her. You would never leave her house. She would lock you in.'

Lucia took me to her surgery where Yamilia waited.

'I know you two,' she said, 'you get back together. Every time.'

She smiled and left the room. Yamilia glared at me.

'Why you close the house?

A few days before a Dutchman who lived in Miramar had phoned me.

'You need to be careful,' he said.

'Of what?'

'Rosa told me about you. She's a friend. You know too many things, too many people. This woman of yours, she can damage you.'

'How?'

'Believe me. In Cuba it happens.'

'What happens?'

'She only needs a piece of your hair, anything of yours.'

'Santeria? Yamilia?'

'Listen to me. I've seen it happen. That's all she needs, some hair, some clothing, anything. Don't laugh at this. She can damage you.'

'Yamilia doesn't know anything about that.'

'Yes, she does. They all do. You are well known. You have enemies. I'm telling you, take this seriously.'

He gave me his address. I promised to visit him, learn how to avoid being cursed and doomed or whatever. I didn't go.

'Why you close the house?'

226

'You know why. Too much trouble.'

We went around and around.

'Where you stay?'

'I can't tell you.'

'With Tony,' she said.

'No.'

'Si, you stay with Tony. You think he help you? You think José help you? You think they are your friends?'

'Jose is my friend, Tony too, I think.'

'Tony.' She spat the word. She mimed someone stepping on an ant. 'He will do this to you.'

'You introduced me to him.'

'Si. Look what he do to me. Now me nothing to him. He only like your money. He will take the house.'

The weight of opinion against her was almost unanimous. From the first moment we'd been together, first José and then nearly everybody else warned me off: 'She's bad.' She's crazy.' 'She's stupid.' 'She's common.' She was bad and crazy. Who isn't? Stupid? No. Common? No. I ignored all of them, defended her, tried to figure out the vested interests – they all had those – against the friendships. I spent a long time picking my friends, or at least people I could work with, and where was I now? What was I left with? I still had most of my money, or so I thought, I never checked. I had a business plan with Paul. I was in good shape. But. Cuba can be exhausting if you don't go with the flow. If you're a stranger, alone, a foreigner without fluent Spanish, it's hard. Yamilia was gone. It was too early to take her back, if at all. I was tired. Tired of all of them. Tired of reading between the lines and watching my back. I couldn't find the space to think clearly. Maybe I just needed some time away from Cubans. The trouble with that was I couldn't go near an airport. Not unless I wanted to spend a week or two in the company of the security police, while we chatted and they caught up with what I'd been doing for the past year.

'I no understand you, Chris.'

I turned to look at her.

'Me good character for you. What you want?'

Her voice had changed; the challenge had gone out of it. Suddenly I just felt very, very sad.

'I don't want any more trouble, Yamilia. Too much trouble.'

'Me too.'

'I need some time.'

'Come to Camaguey. We can stay with my mama. Before, there, no problems.'

'No, there were no problems then.'

'Come to Camaguey. We don't need money there. No Tony, no José, no Havana, no trouble.'

I thought I was going to say, 'Yes, let's go.' But I didn't. I said,

'We do need money Yamilia. You like money. I like money. I need visas. I need to phone England. Your mama's house is too small. We'd have to find somewhere. I need some time.'

She moved away.

'You need some time.'

She'd heard this before, didn't like the sound of it any better now.

'OK. Go to Tony, José. Find perfect woman. Make your business.'

She'd gone as far as she was prepared to go. Further. She got up to leave, opened the door and shouted to Lucia. As soon as she appeared Yamilia started. The hurricane built in strength as she detailed the injustice and ridiculousness of the situation to Lucia. As she shouted Lucia looked sadly between the two of us.

'I'll take you to Havana,' I said.

She looked at me scornfully:

'You think I can't get to Havana?'

She slammed the door and was gone.

José was watching the French Open Tennis when I got back. He poured me a drink as I sat down.

'Capriati,' he said. 'Good game.'

I sat and watched, finished the rum and poured another.

'Jose,' I said, 'I know you don't like Yamilia. I know things would be better for you if she weren't around. Really, what do you think of her?'

'You know what I think. I think she is bad.'

We watched the tennis and finished the bottle.

'You want more?' said José.

'Not here.'

'You want to play pool?'

'I need a woman.'

He brightened. He'd been trying to fix me up with a 'good woman' since I'd come to Cuba. A woman, who would do as she was told, would look after me and not be any trouble.

'The woman I introduced to you,' he said, 'in Chinatown. She is a good woman; she likes you. All the time she asks about you. Not beautiful like Yamilia. You don't need another beautiful woman. This is a good woman.'

'I don't want a good woman tonight, Jose.'

He gave me a look that said, 'She's not *that* good.'

We drove to Havana and parked near Jose's flat. He told me to wait and disappeared into the crowds. Ten minutes later he was back. She was with him.

'I'll see you tomorrow,' he said.

She got into the car. I recognised her, but couldn't remember from where or when. I asked her name. Marita. Mid-twenties, white, very pretty. I asked if she'd like to go for something to eat, a drink, maybe a club. We could go to Villa Pan Americana later.

'Si,' she said, nodding eagerly and smiling.

She settled back into the seat, her body turned towards me as I drove. She laughed, leaned over and put her tongue in my ear. I turned off the malecon into Zueleta, slowed down for the car in front. I noticed movement from the corner of my eye. A car coming from the left, leaving the tunnel roundabout. A bit fast I thought. I turned to look. It *was* fast. I waited for it to slow down. It was bound to. It didn't. I had nowhere to go. It hit me just at the back end of the driver's door. I felt a flash of pain in my left arm before I was thrown forward and sideways at the same time.

I remember thinking: this is a stupid way to die. I remember thinking: I wish I'd had Marita first. I remember seeing the lamp-post coming towards me. I remember my face going through the windscreen and the breath going out of me as my chest hit the dashboard. I remember my right knee hitting something. I remember looking over at Marita as I was thrown back into the seat. She was sitting and watching, sheer horror on her face, but still in the same position. I remember thinking: I'm glad she's not hurt, that would be too much.

Then I remember hands on me and lying in the road with people all around. I tried to get up, but I was a mixture of rubber and pain and blood. I remember one face, a man staring down at me; I watched him as I sank beneath the tarmac into a deep black sea.

I woke in a white room, a bright light in my eyes, faces peering down at me. Something had woken me: it was pain. A nurse was stitching my upper lip back together. I tried to move. A male voice shouted and hands gripped my shoulders. I looked around. There were eight of them, mostly nurses, watching me curiously.

'Buenos noches,' said a female voice.

With effort I lifted my head an inch, looked down at my body. Another voice.

'Take it easy.'

A white towel covered my middle, a tube protruded with yellow liquid draining into a bottle. Another tube taped to my arm from a bottle above the table. The nurses were pretty. I lifted my left arm a little. It felt light.

'Where's my fucking Rolex?'

Some chatter. One of the nurses jangled her wrist. Among the bracelets and bangles was the Rolex. She shook her head and laughed.

'Don't worry,' she said, 'later.'

A doctor was talking to me.

'You have been in an accident, he said. 'You have been drinking.'

'I haven't.'

'Your blood says you have.' He held up some x-rays. 'You have cracked some ribs. Your knee and shin are damaged, maybe your spine too. Many cuts on your face and head, the rest of your body, maybe some scars. We need to look at your head and neck, take some more x-rays. You will have to stay here for some time. You have other injuries. Have you recently been in another accident?'

'Sort of.'

He stared at me and shook his head.

'The security police will want to talk to you.'

The nurses were cleaning me up. One picked pieces of glass from my face and forehead with tweezers, another behind me shaved my head carefully. A new face appeared. He didn't look like a doctor.

'Mr Hilton. You have had a serious accident. You have been drinking.'

'I haven't.'

'The tests say you have. Listen to me.'

I listened.

'Do you have insurance?'

'No'

'This is not a tourist hospital. Some Cuban people brought you here in their car. You will have to pay. How will you pay?

'Do you have my wallet?'

He brought it to me. I showed him the cards.

'OK,' he said.

'We checked with the security police for your hotel.

They have no record of you. Where have you been staying?

'At the Ambos Mundos.'

'The last record is eleven months ago. Where have you been since then?

'Travelling.'

'Where?'

'All over.'

'Where did you stay?'

'Many places. Please, I'm tired. I can't remember.'

'OK, but the security police will want to see you.'

'How is the girl?'

'What girl?'

'Er, the one who found me, helped me from the car.'

'You were with a girl?'

He studied me for a few moments, decided to let it go.

'Is my cellular here?' I said.

'Yes.'

'Can you call someone for me?'

'What is the number?'

I showed him, told him what to say.

Twenty minutes later she was there. She was furious.

'Who you with?' she said.

'Nobody. I was alone.'

'You? Alone in Havana? Me no stupid.'

She looked me over, saw the tube, lifted the sheet and smiled.

'Es pequito,' she said. It's shrunk.

She walked away and spoke with one of the nurses,

demanding information like a ward sister. Back at the bedside she studied my face.

'Senor Frankenstein.'

The nurse behind me said that I needed more stitches. Yamilia went round to watch. The nurse sprayed something on my head and I yelled and nearly leapt from the table. Then I felt the pain in all the other places. Everywhere. The nurse who was wearing my Rolex brought a syringe, spoke to me gently in Spanish as she wiped my arm and pushed it in. I slipped beneath the black sea again.

I opened my eyes to more pain. It was dark. I tried to move my head, but I couldn't lift it or turn to see where I was. I could hear light snoring, somebody moaned in their sleep, a woman. Street voices and music floated up from somewhere. That was no clue. Havana never slept. I tried to remember. The doctor said something about my neck, but I wanted to move, see where I was. I closed my eyes, braced myself, lifted and turned my head. I yelled with the pain. José stirred in the chair by the bed. He smiled sleepily.

'You OK?' he said.

'I'm alive.'

'You look terrible. Your face is cut to pieces.'

'I know. Yamilia said I look like Frankenstein.'

'Yamilia has been here?'

'I called her.'

'Why?'

'I don't know.'

'I do. You are a crazy man.'

He said Tony had been, looked me over, established that

my injuries were 'superficial' and gone off to deal with Rentacar. José got me a private room and brought in some cigarettes and rum. Yamilia appeared once more with some food and disappeared, not to return. Apart from occasional checks from the bad-tempered doctor and nurses peeping in, we were left alone. On the third night he brought Celia.

'You stink,' she said, and took me into the bathroom, helped me to wash.

As we drank and smoked and talked, my pain eased:

'Let's get out of here,' I said.

'Do they know where you stay?'

'I don't think so.'

With a white gown over my bloody, torn clothes I hobbled with their help to a waiting taxi and we went home.

God's away on business.
Tom Waits, song title

PAYBACK

I hardly moved for two weeks, mostly lying on my back while my ribs healed. I read, watched TV and allowed Rosa to fuss around me, Lucia to remove my stitches. I managed to get outside once, but was put off by everyone staring at my face, which was a mass of scabs. I had been lucky though, the facial cuts healed; the top of my head took the main impact and beneath my hair is a mass of scars and dents. If I ever go bald my head will frighten small children.

'Look,' said José, 'they park here when we come to Havana. From here they can see you waiting, see Marita come. You drive to here – he pointed to the junction – here you always wait. They have 100 metres to make some speed, and then bang, they hit you from the side.' I was never convinced of this. If Lazaro and Amado wanted me dead there had to be easier ways. Why would they risk injury to themselves? Even Amado wasn't that stupid.

I didn't like paying for the damage to the other car, which didn't belong to Lazaro or Amado. But I got away with the damage to hire car, which was a write-off. Tony had seen to that. And I'd been drinking. I wasn't drunk, but that wasn't important – by drinking I'd put myself in the wrong, despite the fault being with the other driver. The police and security forces were involved and they wanted something. If they didn't get it I would be escorted to the airport, at best.

Tony chaired the meeting with the police at Rosa's flat; he told them I wasn't yet fit enough to visit the police station. The police had been to Rentacar, who told them where I lived. Tony told Manolo to tell me to keep quiet, he would conduct negotiations. Rosa stood in the kitchen doorway, arms folded, surveying the whole bunch with disdain. I doubted she'd keep quiet. The police tried for an air of seriousness, wearing grave expressions. But Rosa was smart. The table was liberally spread with beer, rum and snacks and despite their attempts at official disapproval a faint party atmosphere slowly developed. Rosa, already popular, kept up the pressure with good-natured cajoling. Tony tried to keep matters on a more serious level, purely business, but even he could see that perhaps this wasn't a bad idea. I did as I was told and kept my mouth shut. I was referred to, pointed at, argued over, accused and defended. Rosa finally addressed me directly,

'Chris, drinking is good while you drink, but it is doing you harm. Especially you. The next day you are not yourself. Your health has been bad. Drink is no good for you. Drink is no good for anybody.'

'Everybody knows that,' I said, 'not many people do anything about it.' The room was silent while they waited for a translation, then, apparently because this was the funniest thing they'd ever heard, the entire room erupted in laughter, regarding me as if I was some mischievous little boy who'd just said something cute. Final attempts at officiousness evaporated. The police left when the drink and food was finished. They didn't take me with them.

They had agreed on a price. The car owners wanted $5000. They got two. The traffic police got something, so did the security police, the tourist police and those present. The people who took me to the hospital didn't ask for anything, but I gave them something anyway, and the guy at Rentacar because I felt sorry for him. The hospital charged me $1200. I didn't begrudge that. There had been a lot of x-rays and tests and besides, I'd had so much free help in the past. In total Tony needed $6000 to secure my freedom. I didn't have it, although I could get $800 per day from ATMs. I told Tony he'd have it in a few days. Don't worry, Tony. Todo control.

Later, José produced an x-ray. He said it was of Marita's thigh. It showed a clean break, the pieces of bone touching with the joins an inch apart. She was OK he said, but her family, who knows? Perhaps a thousand dollars would quash any litigious tendencies.

'José,' I said, 'she phoned me. She's fine. She asked me how I was and suggested we try again, by taxi this time.'

Although he was suitably sheepish, I was a little disappointed. This was by far the worst he'd ever tried that I was aware of. And why now? Did he think I was on the way out, so what the hell? Whatever, it removed any residual guilt about the blow job from Celia while he slept in the back of my car.

238

Living with lust is like living shackled to a lunatic.
Socrates

THE BAD WOMAN

She was dressed in white and played a good game of pool. I was playing for money, a few dollars a game, at the Villa Pan Americana hotel. I played for hours there. I'm pretty good and only improve with alcohol. Up to a point. Before I reached that point I usually won, beating all-comers and making a few dollars. Some challengers just hung around though, waiting until I reached that point.

Anyway, here she was, all in white and hard to beat.

'This is a bad women,' said one of my fellow players. Interesting.

'She's a lesbian,' whispered another.

My cup runneth over.

She offered to play me for five dollars, a lot of money, first to three. She smiled constantly. That is one of the few things I remember. I can remember her playing, her not quite see-through white linen, the struggle I had to beat her and the big grin when she handed over my money – *a ballsy, don't care attitude about her.* Maybe she reminded me of Yamilia, I can't remember, but I had to have her. She seemed amenable.

She spoke no English and merely smiled at my Spanish, whatever I said. About ten of us had been playing. On seeing my intentions they warned me, one by one.

'This is a very bad woman.' And then, 'She is a lesbian,' which was apparently much worse.

Making no headway with me, one of them fetched Dayan, a good friend and professional dancer. He was well-travelled, highly intelligent and spoke fluent English and French.

'Chris, seriously, I must advise you against this. This is a woman with a very bad reputation.'

He didn't add that she was a lesbian. I suppose being well-travelled and highly intelligent he considered it unimportant.

'What can she do to me?' I said.

I couldn't see the problem.

'It's your decision, my friend,' said Dayan, patting my shoulder, 'nobody here will change your mind.'

I listened to José as he spoke into my cellular, patiently explaining in reasonable terms to Tony that we couldn't make the meeting today, that my credit cards had gone. He was nervous. Tony had nominated him as my guardian. There was a pause where I imagined Tony digesting the news. He must have asked where they had gone because I heard José reply, quite openly and honestly, that I had insisted on sleeping with a lesbian the previous night, despite many warnings not to. She had stolen my credit cards. There was a brief pause, José flinched and held the phone away from his face. I could hear Tony shouting from the other side of the room. When the shouting abated José told Tony not to worry, I had cancelled my cards and new ones were on the way. She hadn't had access to cash, not knowing my pin numbers, and had managed to spend just a hundred dollars on shopping before I cancelled the cards. He would have his money shortly. Tony's answer was apparently brief and to the point.

'What shall we do?' said José.

I had no idea. I was hung over and still trying to take it in. I had a few hundred dollars in cash. She hadn't bothered with that, nor my watch or anything else, which was strange – had she calculated a payment scale? Perhaps she thought I'd wake up and had left in a hurry. I thought not. I'd clearly been unconscious and she wasn't the worrying kind.

'You should have left that woman alone,' said José.

I knew that.

Tony got the money two weeks later after the new cards arrived. He asked again if I would move to his house, where he thought there was less scope for trouble. I refused. A few days later Yamilia called my cell phone. She wanted me to meet Lazaro.

'Why?'

'We want to speak with you.'

'He wants the house,' said José when I told him. 'He thought Yamilia owned the house but she didn't. They tried to take it, now he wants to negotiate. Don't meet them.'

'I don't own the house either.'

'You have the authority. Tony protects the house for you.'

'I want to meet him,' I said.

'Why? That is dangerous.'

'I met him once. He's caused me so much trouble. I want to talk to him.'

'Don't do it.'

We spoke to Tony. For the first time I think he doubted my sanity. I explained that I saw Lazaro behind many of my problems. Acknowledging my own culpability, I said that I thought without the interference of Lazaro and Amado life could have worked out very differently, and for the better. I couldn't walk away. I didn't want to fight him, just meet him and see what he had to say.

'Life will still work out differently,' said Tony. 'You can still do everything that you intended, just not with Yamilia. I don't understand your feelings for her. I'm sorry, Chris, she is the most selfish person I have ever met, no class. All that is history. Forget about it. She will work on your feelings. Lazaro is dangerous. You must not meet them.'

'You saw only her attitude to you,' I said. 'Sure, she could be selfish, but do you think I was easy to live with? I'm not a masochist. I stayed with her because I was happy. She was torn. They are dangerous people, but her only security before she met me. I accept that it's finished, but I still believe we could have been happy. I want to meet him.'

They stared in silence.

José and Tony agreed. Don't meet them anywhere they suggest. Meet them in a place of your own choice. Old Havana, somewhere public. Do not agree to anything and do not let them take you anywhere else.

'You must take José for translation.'

'No. I want Yamilia to translate.'

We met at seven in Cathedral Square, full of light and tourists. I watched their approach, Yamilia smart and schoolgirl prim, clearly taking instructions as they walked, dwarfed and cowed in his presence. They came to my table, waited for me to invite them to sit. Lazaro refused my offer of drinks.

'This woman is like a daughter to me,' he said in Spanish.

'That's why she was beaten up in the street.'

He smiled and said nothing. She repeated the sentence. Lazaro listened, inclining his head toward her, the same thin smile I remembered from the night at his house, Magic Night. He spread his arms, a passive but still dismissive gesture, turned abruptly from Yamilia and pulled his chair closer to mine. He leaned forward, as though he wanted to take my hands in his as before. I leaned back. He placed his hands on his knees. His grey eyes seemed unnaturally pale, filled with anger despite his tolerant smile.

'Listen to me,' he said in Spanish, rejecting translation. 'It's history. You are rich. She is not. Why do you want the house? You can buy another house.'

He touched Yamilia's arm.

'Let her have the house. You do not need it.'

He sat back, no longer trying to hide his contempt. He spread his hands,

'What do you say?'

'No.'

'What do you want?'

I want Yamilia. I want you dead. But for you I would give her the house.

'Nothing from you,' I said.

He looked around the square, at the tables of happy tourists, then directly at me. I spoke to Yamilia.

'They would never give the house to you.'

Our eyes met briefly before she turned to him and translated. His shoulders twitched and he looked at the floor. His breath came noisily as he rubbed his hands together.

'Will you stay in Havana?'

'Yes.'

'Then give us the house.'

'No.'

The metal chair screeched against the cobblestones as he pushed it back with his legs.

'Vamos,' he said to Yamilia.

I watched them walk across the square and disappear in a crowded street. Neither of them looked back.

All history is sex and violence.
Ian Fleming

JARED

With Yamilia gone I began to spend time with Celia, especially when José wandered Havana in search of business. She was easy company and wanted nothing from me, often visiting the flat. One day we were due to meet José after Celia's appointment with Lucia in her surgery. He was not alone when we arrived at the Ambos Mundos.

'This is Jared,' he said, introducing me to a short, slightly overweight tourist. 'He is from Jordan.'

Jared had small, black, close together eyes. He offered a damp, limp palm. His eyes made no contact with mine, looking past me at Celia. His kiss on her cheek was too enthusiastic. She darkened with anger. I bought drinks. Jared accepted his without a glance at me, all his interest with Celia. She wore old jeans and a t-shirt because she had a hair and manicure appointment later. She regarded him with an open hostility that he didn't notice. José noticed though, and perhaps to avoid a scene, he wound up his business. Another scrap of paper, another name, another number for his collection.

'He fuck me with his eyes,' said Celia.

Not in a pleasant way either, I gathered. Celia and José had a quick exchange about the quality of his company. I caught the word vulgar.

'What's your business with him?' I said.

'Not too much. He wants to buy something. I gave him a name.'

Celia left saying she would be three hours. Hair and manicure appointments were social occasions too.

'Three hours English time?' I said when she'd gone.

'No.'

'OK, Cuban time – seven hours?'

'About that,' he said.

We made some calls. José gave me the money for the last week, as always a little short. As long as it stayed at a little I ignored it. We spent the afternoon at a rooftop bar, shaded, in a strong breeze, chatting and watching the ferries chugging back and forth across the harbour.

José told me a story of the ferry. Some passengers hijacked it and took it to Florida, including those who didn't want to go. Most of the passengers returned to Cuba. Now the ferries were only allowed enough fuel for each single crossing to prevent it happening again. Celia returned five hours later, her nails shiny and black. She was still angry about Jared.

'You want me to fight him in the hotel, Celia? Forget him.'

She wasn't impressed.

'It's just business, Celia. He is not my friend.'

Business or not. Friend or foe. Jared was dead within the month.

Sex with love is the greatest thing in life. But sex without love – that's not so bad either.
Mae West

A Trip to the Bank

The ATMs in Havana were out of cash. At a bank I asked for five hundred dollars. The cashier, a brunette with a sinful smile, slowly counted out my twenties, licking her fingers before peeling off each note, holding my eyes with a gifted twinkle. I walked to the Ambos Mundos, ordered rum and settled down by the window to read my book. I must have had a busy night because I woke in a room at the Florida hotel. I didn't have much money left so I returned to the same bank. The same cashier greeted me, raised her perfectly sculpted eyebrows as I asked for a further five hundred dollars.

'Por esta noche?' she said. For tonight?

'Si.'

'Can I come?'

'OK.'

The eyebrows relaxed, the eyes shone, the smile, promising much, widened.

Nobody knows anything.
William Goldman

PAUL AGAIN

Paul arrived for our appointment with Rumbos. He was
more relaxed, more open to Cuba, less irritable. Perhaps
we had evened out at similar levels of alcoholism and
so clashed less than before. Rosa eyed him with mistrust, convinced that my drawn-out fall from grace was
his fault. It wasn't, of course, but she could no longer
blame Yamilia. Tony enjoyed Paul's company, while mis-
trusting anybody who drank so much. Paul arrived as
a drunk. I had contrived a slow descent; many people
still saw in me the bright-eyed arrival of the previous
year.

The meeting with Rumbos was for the following week.
Paul said he had obtained an ABTA and was well on his
way to recruiting customers. He favoured the City for likely
takers of our Cuban experience. We made our plans. At
a certain hour and level of intoxication we believed completely in our business with Rumbos. We drew up lists of
prospective employees and decided on their wages, which
Paul always considered too generous. He also crossed out
most of the women I added.

'With men we can expect a low level of embezzlement and allow for it,' he said, 'women cause chaos.'

I disagreed.

'Right, so give us the benefit of your wisdom on how you maintained such a smooth, rewarding relationship with Yamilia and all the success it brought you.'

'You don't understand.'

'True.'

Paul, still having seen little of Cuba, had grown fond of certain aspects – no extradition, its proximity to the Caymans – and he opened a bank account.

'How much money do you have left?' he said.

'I've no idea.'

'It might be a good idea to check.'

'No. That would be unlucky, I think I've been living on my income here and not spending too much. I got through about fifty thousand in the first few months. It's settled down since then. Anyway, we'll be rich soon.'

'What about Cubacell? You made rather a lot of early morning calls. And not just to me, I gather.'

'Not that many. Not a problem.'

'Sure you remember them all?'

Paul finally summoned the courage to approach a Cuban woman, suitably pale. We asked him how it went:

'She offered me $5000 dollars to take her out of the country,' he said. 'I sense a business opportunity.'

At first I used diazepam to sleep, then to deal with anything uncomfortable, which came to mean getting up in the morning. It added to a general sense of unreality, disassociation and a stubborn refusal to review my finances. I began to drive around alone, finding different bars and talking to strangers, wanting something to happen, maybe trying to make something happen. Paul stuck to the big hotels, with José as his chaperone. He could get lost in his own house.

José called from the Habana Libre. Paul became panicky if I stayed away too long. They were having a late drink if I cared to join them. I left the bar and the TV baseball and drove to meet them. Once the Havana Hilton, built by the mob just before the revolution, the hotel's character was its history, still palpable everywhere. The Vegas like structure had been taken over by the revolutionaries, horses in the elevators, wandering from room to room as their masters celebrated. Despite the large numbers of tourists and the shopping precinct it couldn't shake off its air of criminality and rebellion. The lobby was full of men with young women at their sides. At the far end a few women and girls sat together, nursing single drinks for hours, hoping to attract some interest.

Paul and José sat by a window, giving them a clear view of the entire lobby, the entrance, the elevators – all the comings and goings of the hotel. This was Paul's favourite pastime, people watching, dodgy people watching, speculating on the nature of the desire and corruption surrounding us.

'This is more like it,' said Paul, 'why didn't you bring me here before?'

A few feet away an elderly man sat alone. Red-faced and balding, his remaining white hair grew wild and curly, protruding above his ears. He was furious, staring angrily at each table in turn, seemingly disgusted at the sight of so many beautiful girls with so many middle-aged men. This was his holiday hotel and the lobby had turned into a bordello. He caught me looking. His outraged expression accused me: Are you the same? Is that what you're here for?

José gave his interpretation of the various interactions. Paul was quite capable of suddenly joining a table, asking directly what people were up to; corrupt to the core himself, this was his world. I turned away from the angry man. In the centre of the lobby by the circular bar sat a group of six men, each with a Cuban girl sitting decorously at their side. Their confident English voices carried to us and the surrounding area, knowing they could be heard, but arrogant enough not to care. They ignored the girls. Television and films perhaps, producers and fixers; the money side of things. They spoke deals, dropped names, laughed loudly at each other's jokes.

I knew one of the faces, not the name, just that at some time he had appeared on TV, branding his face into my memory. He talked now, leaning forward, a big man emphasising his words with expansive sweeps of his hands, laughing to prompt the others, who laughed to order. The girl next to him was black and professionally pretty. She appeared to possess more energy than the other girls, who sat, in bored docility, waiting for their time. She seemed impatient, as though she wanted something, or she was merely confident enough to challenge him. She began to talk, interrupting his conversation. He continued as if she wasn't there. She persisted, either believing that he couldn't hear or just wanting to be heard. The other girls lowered their heads; the men became silent, no longer laughing on cue. A fug of tension, tangible as the clouds of their cigarette smoke hung over the table.

Paul and José watched the same scene, as were others around us. José raised his eyebrows at me; he knew what was coming. Paul too had tuned in. The girl began to tug the man's sleeve.

'Don't do that, love,' said Paul. She continued to tug at his sleeve, repeating the same phrase in a persistent tone, unaware of the atmosphere around her. He backhanded her across the face, neither turning to look at her nor interrupting the flow of his conversation. She looked around wide-eyed, awake for the first time to the stares and the other girls' lowered heads. A trickle of blood ran from the corner of her mouth. Her confidence evaporated as she fumbled in her bag for a tissue, which she held to her mouth to keep the blood from her clothes.

A hum of conversation rose around us. Show over. The lone, bald, angry man looked apoplectically about him, as though expecting someone to do something, something more to happen. Nothing happened. He stood, knocking his chair back noisily and left the lobby, firing accusing stares at anyone in his path. Nobody noticed him. José shook his head, feigning nonchalant indifference, but he was angry, something deep inside him hurt and outraged.

'Charming,' said Paul.

I nursed a fantasy of the table of men alone, without hotel security, police or money to protect them, alone with José and some friends. I wondered if they would last a minute before their smug superiority turned to whining, shitting-themselves panic.

We met Tony at his house the next day to be briefed for

our meeting with Rumbos. We sat mutely as Manolo translated his instructions. Tony seemed encouraged by our silence, took it as a sign of concentration.

'Todo control,' said Tony smiling, as we walked to the taxi.

I gave him the thumbs up.

'Todo control, Tony.'

I had swallowed two diazepam washed down with rum just to be capable of leaving the flat. Paul was a walking corpse, white-faced and red-eyed, he clung to my laptop like a life-belt.

We were shown into a large office at Rumbos. Alicia, a pretty, smiley woman of around thirty introduced herself. She was very pleased to meet us and would do her best to help us with our ambitions. She had a pile of brochures and documents on her desk. Charming, cheerful and thorough, she glanced occasionally at Paul, who hadn't spoken. She seemed to accept him as the financial man, calculating the figures, the silent type. He tapped at the keyboard pointlessly, hands shaking behind the screen. I listened but heard nothing. The angel on my right shoulder said: This is fantastic and easily possible; you could be millionaires. On my left, the devil said: You had diazepam and rum for breakfast. Your partner is incapable of speech. This is going nowhere.

Paul's screen had gone blank, the battery dead. He continued to tap away, refusing to meet my eyes. Alicia continued unperturbed, smiling and chirpy, fastidiously explaining every detail, perhaps thinking that all English businessmen were like this: cool and distant. Wrecked. This was a great opportunity, she told us. Rumbos would do most of the work if we supplied the tourists. There was money to be made for us. Fifty-fifty with Fidel, of course. And unlimited scope for the future. I concentrated on her cleavage; it felt like the only way to stay sane.

We left, apparently with their blessings and high hopes for the future. I had an armful of documents. Alicia called us a taxi. As the taxi pulled away I turned to Paul, waved the pile of stuff at him,

'What do you think,' I said.

'Can we stop at a bar?'

'You were a great help,' I said.

'Right, and your magnificent negotiating skills were a brilliant success. All you did was stare at her tits. This is pointless.'

'It can work. We need a plan of action.'

'I don't want it to work. I hate this fucking country. I don't want to work here. I don't want to work, full-stop.'

'You don't have to work here. I'll do that.'

'Right, here we are, before midday, drinking ourselves back to some semblance of normality. You going to be any different next week?'

José joined us.

'What happened? I have to call Tony,' he said.

Paul snorted.

'Tell him it went well,' I said, 'tell him Paul will set everything up in England, then we'll meet them again.'

'True?' he said.

'No.'

'I can sober up. Can you?' I said.

'You can't and no.'

'You're just in a bad mood. We can sleep on this and take another look at it.'

'No, we can't. I don't want to. It won't work. You can't get anything done here. I don't fucking like it here.'

'You like the rum.'

'I can buy that in Oddbins. The people are rude. I hate the fucking food. I detest the fucking music.'

'Maybe it will grow on you.'

'Fuck off.'

We took another taxi to the Ambos Mundos. With rum Paul began to reconsider. I went to the bar for drinks. Next to me an American was doing the same.

'You English?'

It turned out I was. He said he visited Cuba regularly. He was a baseball coach and made trips to Cuba, arranging games between American and Cuban kids.

'They allow you to do that?'

'It's charity, by invitation of the Cuban government, yeh, I'm allowed. I spend three or four months of the year here. You on vacation?'

'I live here.'

'You live here? That must take some arranging. You got real estate here?'

'A house in Guanabacoa.'

'Guanabacoa, where's that?'

'A few miles, just the other side of the harbour.'

'I'm Rob.' He extended a hand.

Of similar age to me, short in a too tight shirt that hugged his paunch, he sported a black, untidy moustache on a round red face. He stayed at the bar with me. At his table I noticed his helper, slick, well-dressed, black on black, menacing and attentive. Cool. His woman, also black, sleek, expensive and bored sat gazing through the window.

'I'm looking to buy a house here. Save on renting. Need a base here. You interested in selling?'

'Maybe.'

I described the house, honestly I thought, in glowing terms.

'Can I take a look?'

'Sure.'

Would Tony help me sell the house? Of course he would if there was a profit in it. I spoke to José. Did he think it was possible? He did. OK, I'll make an appointment. Paul and José returned with me to the bar.

'OK. When would you like to see the house?'

'Soon as. Tomorrow good for you?'

'We can do that.'

We went straight to Tony's. He wasn't exactly enthusiastic, but his nose for a profit won through. He'd open the house tomorrow. Me, Tony and Manolo would wait at the house while Paul and José took a taxi to fetch Rob.

I arrived at the house with Tony. The house, which I hadn't seen in six months, was clean and tidy. All the furniture I'd bought with Yamilia was still there. It looked much the same. I'd had some rum and two diazepam before leaving home. I asked Maria for a rum at the house. She served me morosely.

'Slowly, Chris,' said Tony.

'No problem.'

'And how is the she-devil?' said Manolo.

'You're so funny, Manolo, such a comedian.'

Chuchi arrived and exchanged brief angry words with Tony before leaving again.

'Problem, Tony?'

He shook his head. Manolo said nothing.

Paul and José arrived in a mini-bus taxi. Rob had brought his entourage. We sat in the large entrance hall. Rum, beer and coffee were offered. Rob looked flustered and uncomfortable. His minder stood impassively by the door. He spoke only to his man, into his ear before stepping back. He made no eye contact with anyone else. His woman looked around her with open disgust. Tony had asked that he, with Manolo's help should do the required negotiating – we were going to try for fifteen and accept twelve. José beckoned me to the kitchen.

'The tunnel was closed,' he said.

The tunnel under the harbour was the quick way, on a good day a twenty-minute drive from Havana. The taxi had been forced to take the slow way, in heavy traffic, forty-five minutes.

'And Paul never stop talking,' he said, 'he talk too much.'

Back in the lobby things were not going well.

'This is a little too far for me,' said Rob, 'I need somewhere with quicker access to Havana.'

Perhaps a better price would tempt him? If I threw in the furniture? He didn't say no outright. We were still discussing terms when Chuchi returned with a local CDR guy. He launched into a shouted monologue directed at Tony. Tony seemed unperturbed, making only occasional contemptuous replies. Chuchi stood in the background, his horrible smile in place, nodding in agreement with everything his new friend said. The CDR guy wound up with a flourish and they left.

'Well, I'm outa here,' said Rob, and he and his entourage were gone.

'Mi otro casa,' said Tony, 'ahora.' My other house. Now. I drove with José, Paul and Manolo.

'That went well,' said Manolo.

At Tony's house Paul, José, Manolo and I shared a bottle of rum. Tony asked for a glass and a cigarette to go with it.

'That was not clever. Your moves lately, they are not clever,' said Manolo.

'He was never going to buy it,' I said. 'Tony, is there a problem with the CDR?'

He dismissed it with a sweep of his hand, as though shaking off an insect. He was drinking and smoking though.

'Chris,' said Tony in his biggest voice. He spoke to Manolo, asked him to translate.

'Your drinking is a problem.'

Manolo, José and even Paul nodded their agreement.

'*My* drinking is a problem?'

'You are the one who lives here. You are making trouble for yourself. Too much rum and too many women. You will drive yourself crazy. If you are to succeed here it must stop.'

Again he received complete agreement from his audience. I glared at José. He shrugged.

'I think you must leave Rosa. Live here. You pay minimum rent. We can work together and make sure our plans, your plans, succeed.'

'I like it at Rosa's.'

'I know you like it at Rosa's,' he shouted. Tony had never shouted at me before. 'So do the hospitals, the doctors and nurses and the police and Rentacar and every chica in Havana! And you will make trouble for me too. No. You want my help you stay here and you only drink beer. No more rum.'

'I don't like beer.'

'Then drink fucking mojitos. No more straight rum. And stop the diazepam, you don't need them. José, don't give him any more. You're his friend. Keep him out of trouble or don't come back to this house.'

José nodded. Paul giggled.

'Fuck off.'

'And find yourself a good woman. I know you suffered when Yamilia left, but you're a big man now. Find a good chica who will not be any trouble.'

'No more she-devils,' said Manolo.

'You can shut the fuck up. Mr Happy.'

'Que?' said Tony.

José translated. Tony laughed, stood up and ruffled my hair. He ignored Manolo and used José to translate.

'Chris, Chris. It's OK. But you must slow down. At Rentacar they call you the man with more lives than a cat. That's enough, don't use up any more, please.'

He laughed and asked for more rum and another cigarette. I agreed to the conditions, except for leaving Rosa. Everyone sat around drinking, chatting and smiling. Except Manolo, he didn't smile at all. He was silent, staring at me with utter hatred in his eyes.

If we knew the truth about each other we could take no one seriously. There isn't one among us who could afford to be caught. That's all life is. Trying not to be caught out.
Willie Donaldson

JOSÉ GOES TO PRISON

I slowed down. I gave Paul a book list when he left and when they arrived I spent my days at the pool reading. Rosa cooked in the evenings and we watched DVDs. She made weak mojitos. Anxious not to lose me to Tony she spoiled me. Lucia brought her family again and life became similar to my early days here. Only Yamilia was missing. I knew she stayed in touch with Lucia, who, as one of the few people who thought we were good for each other, tried to set up a meeting. I said no, but I thought about her all the time.

Celia called my cellular.

'Is José. The police take him.'

'Why?'

'I don't know. They come for him today.'

I took a taxi to José's flat. I'd never been there before, which was strange. It was very small, but all his. Most Cubans live with several family members. To live alone takes effort and resources. His clothes hung on a wooden stand-alone rail. I recognised some of the stuff I'd given to him.

'First we need to find out where he is,' I said.

It took a day of phone-calls. José was arrested with over twenty others in a massive swoop throughout Havana. He was in prison, and no, we couldn't visit. We still had no idea what he was supposed to have done. I didn't want to ask Tony for help, not yet anyway; I wasn't doing much to please him lately, although he still had an income from my cars. I tried the British Embassy. I don't know what I thought they could do.

They received me with cool politeness. Apparently this, whatever it was, was a situation they did not want to be concerned with. The fact that I was associated with these people made me someone they didn't want to be concerned with either. The Cubans could do as they wished with them and the less heard about it the better. And I left with the veiled, but nevertheless, clear warning: 'Watch yourself. What do you think you are doing? Do you think you are immune? Behave or leave or you will join them. And we won't do anything for you either.'

Reluctantly, we tried a police station. They asked me, but not Celia, to leave. I waited for two hours. In the taxi she spoke in a flat monotone.

'The Jordanian man, he is dead. Some people killed him and put him under their patio. José's phone number was in his wallet. They have arrested all the people whose names they found with that man.'

She didn't like Jared any the better for being dead.

'Three people, they strangle and kill him. The American cut him here.'

She drew a line across her throat.

'The American?'

'Andy,' she said.

A patrol car followed us openly until we got to the flat. Celia got out and I asked the driver to take me to the Inglaterra where I sat on the terrace nursing a drink until the police got bored and drove away. Then I walked back to the flat.

She repeated what she knew in a voice, dull with shock: The death of a man, an idiot abroad, who played at being a gangster and had the bad luck to run into Andy, and José, who had the bad luck to run into both of them. She struggled to speak as the enormity of the repercussions for José began to sink in. I poured her a drink. I thought for a moment she was going to refuse, but in her confusion she just hadn't seen it. She finished it in two gulps and asked for another.

'Can we see him?'

She shook her head:

'Impossible.'

We went to see Tony.

On the malecon a pelican, blown ashore and lumbering desperately to get airborne, flew directly at our taxi. Two boys chased it, making grabs for its legs as it tried, in dreamy slow motion, to escape. Finally, gaining some momentum, its feet brushed our window as it rose, leaving the two boys sprawled across the bonnet, giggling at us through the windscreen. We laughed back at them. Two policemen stood at the next junction. They were laughing too.

Tony went berserk. This would hurt him, he didn't want to be involved. He shouted at me in Spanish as Manolo translated. He is not worth it. He's just a gofer. He is unreliable. His own stupidity got him where he is. This is bad for you. It will make them take an interest in you. Even more interest. And in me too. He jabbed his chest. In me too.

'He's my friend, Tony.'

'Your friend? Did you like his trick with the x-rays?'

Celia nudged me. Tony had barely acknowledged her. What was this about x-rays? I explained. She shook her head. Tony seemed to notice her for the first time.

'Ay, chica,' he said.

He sat down next to her. In his soothing baritone he repeated what he'd just shouted at me.

'Ay, chica.'

'Her name is Celia,' I said.

'Celia,' he repeated sadly. He stood and put a hand on her shoulder, shaking his head.

I told Manolo to translate my words exactly.

'Tony, the first time I met you I gave you one hundred dollars. As a gesture of faith.'

He began to protest.

'Let me finish. Listen. Every time we went for meals with you, for pleasure or business, you took half the bill as your cut. They charged me tourist prices every time. When your sister Loli helped with Rumbos and advice about the business, I gave her five hundred dollars. Did she keep it all? You're making at least two hundred dollars a week from the cars I bought. The wardrobe you sold me wasn't worth even half what I paid you. Same with the

DVD player your son sold me. You took a percentage of Yamilia's video business. I set that up, you had nothing to do with it.'

Silence filled the room. Tony fixed me with his pale green eyes, hands on his knees. Celia tried to disappear behind me. Manolo tilted his chin at me: You through yet? I wasn't.

'You took your cut from the house, from the police, from Rentacar. The fifteen dollars rent you charged me when I was here with Yamilia – you gave five dollars back to her, every day.'

'She insisted,' he said.

'You should have told me. You didn't even like her.'

'He hated her,' said Manolo.

'You should have told me. I'd have left her sooner. And there's more, and then more again that I don't know about.'

'You'd be in prison without him,' said Manolo.

'I know that. And who asked you, errand boy? José is where he is because he gave his phone number to the wrong person. That's all it is. I know you don't think much of him, but he doesn't deserve this. I can't do much, but I'll pay to get him out. You can help. Let me know what it costs.'

Manolo started to speak, but Tony hushed him with an impatient wave of his hand.

'I will speak to some people,' he said, 'see if we can discover what's happening.'

'It's not just money this time,' said Manolo.

'No speak,' said Tony. He made a zipping motion across his mouth.

'He must keep his mouth shut,' said Manolo, 'they need him to admit something.'

'And chica, Celia,' said Tony, nodding at me, 'keep him from trouble. Please.'

In the taxi Celia breathed a long sigh.

'I don't believe José did that with the x-ray,' she said.

Freed from uncertainty, Celia quickly adapted. José would not be around for a while. That was that. We had a few drinks at the flat and, for a change of atmosphere went to see *Salome* at the Havana Theatre. As we walked home Celia said,

'Yamilia is Salome.'

'But I still have my head.'

Back at José's flat she poured our drinks. Her taste for rum would not help my efforts to reform.

'Even if Tony help José for nothing this will cost you more money.'

She pronounced 'nurthing' and 'murney' in her slow, smoky drawl.

'I know.'

If he could help. How much would it cost? How much had I spent? What did I have left?

'Celia,' I said.

'Si?'

'I don't think I have much money left.'

She threw her head back and laughed.

Jose's flat became home. For now. Because Celia didn't want to be alone. Because I didn't want to be alone. Because we could be of more help to José together. I found it odd how uncomfortable Celia seemed in Havana, never fully at ease, as though she was expecting something awful to happen. Well, maybe not so strange because it had. In

José's flat or wherever I was staying, she relaxed and was herself, but on the streets, in bars, anywhere public, she became quiet and timid. Having seen the confidence she displayed in Santiago, this was baffling. Baffling and attractive; it drew me powerfully to her. I could never be sure if it was my predator's instinct for female weakness or the need to protect her. Both, probably.

She rarely wore makeup. Her eyebrows were trimmed, she had one stud earring in her left ear and she did nothing with her hair other than keep it very short. It was like a form of brutal honesty – this is me, take it or leave it. She wasn't beautiful, nowhere near, but I felt a strong attraction. She wore only jeans or short skirts with skimpy tops, but carelessly, not in any look at me way. When we went dancing she wore a sort of soft trilby and a man's jacket. I found myself looking at her often, not looking away easily, thinking about the rest of those lovely slim legs and her small bra-less breasts. She looked straight back, laughing her smoker's, knowing laugh, delighted at the weakness of men. Her brown eyes were warm and amused, sometimes frightened. She was gentle, seemed to yearn for gentleness in the macho, biting, scratching, swearing world of Cuban sex. Tears sometimes appeared in her eyes – she didn't sob – tears would just roll down her cheeks. She wept without knowing.

We lay on José's bed, through the blinds the evening sun dappled the dark and off-white of our bodies. I felt a twinge of something vaguely unpleasant, perhaps the dregs of my conscience. I said as much to Celia. She smiled,

'Chris, José is not here,' she said.

266

She kissed my chest.
'You think too much,' she said.
'OK, no more thinking.'

Oh, everything looks bad if you remember it.
Homer Simpson

ISABEL VISITS

The ringing phone woke us early. Celia picked it up, listened and replaced the receiver without speaking.

'Isabel is here', she said, 'she wants to talk to you.'

'Where is she?'

'Here. We can walk. Five minutes.'

She sat on the sea wall of the malecon, her back to the sea, staring through, rather than at, the teeming crowds. She had just hitched from Santiago. Some Mexican tourists had crashed one of our cars, which was a write-off. No serious injuries and they would claim on holiday insurance. But the police were involved. They found out where the car was hired. The other five cars were impounded. It should have meant serious trouble for those involved, but Isabel's father had smoothed things out, although the business was finished. Isabel had come to tell me and to warn us.

'So you are all OK, nobody is in trouble?'

'We are all OK.'

'Do they know who paid for the cars?'

'No.'

'So they don't know my name, they don't know who I am?'

She shook her head, but exchanged the briefest of glances with Celia.

'OK, so what now?'

'Nothing now. It is finished.'

So why had she come? A phone call could have covered this.

'I came to give you this,' she said.

She handed me a bundle of notes, maybe five hundred dollars. I offered some of it to her. 'For your journey.'

'Keep it. You will need it more than me.'

She asked something of Celia. They spoke rapidly, but I caught Yamilia's name. Isabel turned and studied me for a few seconds, the usual severe expression, dark eyes bright with calculation. I held her gaze. She jerked her head and turned away, as though I'd made an obscene suggestion.

She joined a queue waiting for lifts. After a few minutes a truck stopped, a few Cubans already standing and sitting in the back. A small crowd spoke to the driver, some walked away, others climbed up, including Isabel. As the truck pulled away she stood in the front corner, her hands on the cab, her long black hair blowing behind her as she stared at the sea. She didn't look back.

I saw her weeks later on television, part of a group of young Cubans off to Columbia to lend their medical skills. She spoke confidently to camera, explaining their task to the Cuban people. They were filmed at a farewell dance to celebrate the trip. The camera panned the dancers, smiling faces filled the screen. The view widened. Isabel stood alone in isolated bafflement at the jollity around her.

It is agreed then, that I shall not kill myself till two or three days hence.
Candide

BROKE

Tony said I could do nothing for José concerning the charges – accomplice to murder – but that a thousand dollars might speed up the process, get the case to court quicker. Tony suspended our car business because of the attention and Santiago was finished. I had no income. I told him to sell our cars and pay whoever needed to be paid, to take whatever rent and visa money he was owed. He didn't want to sell. I convinced him that greater funds would soon be forthcoming from Paul and, for now, I needed the cash. I wanted to gather whatever I had and put it in a Havana bank. Take stock. Make a new plan.

Since I had lost the money to the United States Treasury I had found another route. The commission was extortionate, but at least the money arrived. I could transfer it in lumps of £5000 from my offshore account. I didn't want to empty the account as I still hoped to use it in the future. I hadn't spoken to them in months, merely taking what I needed from ATMs. I phoned them from my cellular while Celia slept. I asked them to send me $5000.

'You don't have $5000, said a voice.'

'That can't be right.'

'It is. You have £2576 left in your account.'

I argued with the voice. The voice didn't want to be wasting its time with someone who had to worry about a few thousand pounds; it had rich customers to deal with. The voice had been very polite when I opened the account: it didn't like me anymore. I argued about the $27000 confiscated in transit by the Americans, but the voice denied responsibility. It couldn't have known about the change in the law. The voice wanted me off the phone. My chest was hurting and I needed to think. I told the voice to send me the £2576.

The sudden realisation that I'd blown it tried to enter my consciousness. Tried to enter. I didn't allow it in because I needed to think. What was I going to do? I made coffee and topped it up with rum. Tony would sell the three cars. A thousand for him to keep him sweet and the same for José's case. With the last of the Jersey money and what Isabel had brought, I'd have about $10000. I took a coffee and some toast into Celia. She ignored the toast and sipped the coffee.

'There is rum in here,' she said.

'You will need it.'

'Why? What happened?'

'My money has gone.'

She showed no concern or surprise.

'You will be OK. You must live like a Cuban now. You can do it again. Make some more money. Then you will know what to do. You have had your education. Many people who comes to Cuba goes crazy, lose all their money and get deported. You are still here.'

She poured two tall glasses of rum.

'Here. Only one, too early for more. So, we have no money.'

'Maybe $10000 left.'

She spat her coffee.

'Chris, I could live for years with that.'

But I couldn't. And neither could she. Not with me.

We tried. We bought from the markets and cooked in the flat. Rum is cheap, but costs mount when you drink it every day. I had to meet Tony regularly and though we once spent hours hitching out to see him, we soon reverted to taxis. We stayed in and watched DVDs during the week, but Saturday nights we went out. Then rum, and sometimes coke, made us invincible and money drained away with the night. I didn't tell Tony how broke I was. He was pleased to see the attempt at frugal living and keen to get back to business with some new cars. I stalled, saying that I was waiting for a large payment from England. I did tell Paul, conscious for the first time of the cost of my calls.

'What have you done with it all?'

He sounded like an indignant parent, scolding a child for spending all their pocket money. I didn't say anything. When he finished lecturing me, I said,

'So I'm short of cash. Can you help?'

'I'll see what I can do.'

'Bring a card I can use or some cash. I'll pay you back if you want out. I just need to get started again.'

'OK. Will do.'

'Did you call my mother and the others, tell them I'm OK?'

'Yes.'

I believe we've had all the fun we can expect here.
Charles Ryder: Brideshead Revisited

TRIAL

José had been in prison for nine weeks when, on a Friday, Tony phoned to say the case was going to court. The trial would begin on Monday. Tony was uncharacteristically optimistic. José, according to his sources had said nothing, so he could be charged with no more than having someone's phone number in his wallet – a very, very minor accessory, if that. Possibly a light sentence or some form of probation, but José was well known and far from innocent in other areas, so there was always a danger of punishment for crimes, real or imagined. There was public access but Tony asked us, particularly me, to stay away. My money had helped to speed up the process, but there was nothing else we could do. We could only wait.

We waited at a roof bar overlooking the harbour, sheltered from the summer sun by a canopy, and grateful for a tiny breeze from the sea. Even thinking sapped the energy. Most of Havana would be unbearable. It was Saturday, late afternoon and we were waiting for the evening, the cool and the dark, the time to drink, dance and forget. We had been sipping slowly for a few hours, drinking water too and were just ordering food. Neither of us had much appetite but rum on an empty stomach is certain to end in nausea. Celia was a good drinking partner. Relaxed in each other's company, we talked easily but were comfortable with silence.

We both liked people watching and inventing lives for them. Celia never really got drunk, she would just decide at some stage, usually late, that she had to sleep, and she would.

'Chris, how much money do you have?'

'Not much, a few hundred dollars.'

'And that is it, finished?

'Yes, until Paul sends more.'

'Let's go out tonight, have a good time. Finish it now.'

And forget Monday and José for a few hours.

We took a taxi to Tony's house for my best suit and shoes. We bought a long, low cut, blue silk dress at the Habana Libre. She never wore high heels and settled for some white leather sandals. At home she gelled her short hair and combed it flat. She tried on the dress, twirled in front of the mirror, the evening sun revealing glimpses of her body beneath.

'Can you see if I wear anything under the dress?'

She wore the briefest of thongs and no bra, but I couldn't tell. At certain points the light seemed to reveal all, a tantalising hint of nakedness and promise which vanished in a second as the silk became sheer. I stared as she danced, waiting and wanting further glimpses of her despite her availability to me. She would be stared at constantly tonight by other men, teasing them as they, trapped by their own nature and desires, tried to see something that would vanish as they stared. And she would smile happily, feigning indifference.

'I can't see,' I said, 'sometimes I think yes, sometimes I think no.'

'Perfect.'

When I was ready she adjusted me to her satisfaction and stood beside me in front of the mirror.

'Mmm, elegant. We are ready.'

At La Catedral we were the object of disapproving glares from tourists. I'd been used to it with Yamilia, but this was the first time with Celia. She noticed too.

'Why do they stare?'

'Because I'm exploiting you.'

'Exploiting?'

'Taking advantage of your innocence, using you because you are poor.'

She laughed until tears ran down her cheeks, looking directly at the tourists until they turned away.

A new club had sprung up in the narrow warren of streets around Obispo. Derelict a few weeks ago, it had been fitted with a long narrow bar, colourful murals on the lower walls and low multi-coloured lights to hide the emptiness above – there was no roof, just a hastily erected canopy. There was a small dance area and a pool table; two bouncers ensured the payment of a three-dollar entrance fee to keep it exclusive. The place was full and it all felt new, wicked and exciting. We danced, played pool and got slowly very drunk. As my money vanished I yearned to prolong this life: the crush of people, the sharp reek of tobacco, perfume, the brilliant smiles, the smell of rum and sex.

'Let's stay at the Nacional,' she said, at two in the morning.

'OK.'

From the taxi I watched clothes drying on the balconies along the malecon. They were blowing horizontally. The air had cooled, the sea angry and spraying the wide path and one lane of traffic. We slowed as a policeman diverted us into the far lane. He looked into the taxi, shone a torch at me and then waved us on. I asked Celia for a cigarette. She didn't answer, her face between her knees as she sniffed from the tiny mirror she kept in her bag.

It cost a ridiculous amount to get Celia into the hotel. It didn't matter. If I was broke today, tomorrow or the next day – what difference did it make? We ate to keep the drunkenness at bay, the rooftop restaurant almost empty. I recognised an actor with three girls, passing round cocaine, smoking, laughing, drinking, secure in his affluence. He didn't give us a glance, although the girls did. Who was I? Who was the skinny girl? What were we doing here? We were spending the last of our money and tomorrow we would be poorer than them.

A slow ballad began. Cuban ballads could sound so good, break your heart without needing to understand a word, beautiful voices full of yearning. I translated a few songs, and now they took on a different meaning. Verses like: 'Ay, my beautiful Maria, when you walk along the beach, the way the cheeks of your ass move makes me feel horny,' or the popular song of the moment, played everywhere: 'Papaya con dolor': Cunt of Pain. Celia hummed and sang into my shoulder as we held each other upright. In the background the sea lashed the sea wall and the road with explosive cracks. The sky was low, the night grey and black, the lights of a tanker just visible as it made its slow passage along the horizon. Parts of Havana were blacked out with the usual power cuts in the poorer areas – the tourist spots and the hotels shone on in the gloom.

I felt as free as I thought anyone could be. I had more freedom than the Hollywood actor with his nose on the table. He couldn't leave the hotel, he didn't know where to go; he couldn't go anywhere because he didn't know anybody or know what to do. I could mix with them and meet the same women they did. And I could leave, find the cheapest of peso bars and spend the night with a real senorita. Or I could just go home.

The face is familiar, but I can't remember my name.
Robert Benchley

WHERE AM I?

My head felt like a beaten anvil, a blacksmith shaped hot metal inside my skull. It was already uncomfortably hot and heading for intolerable. I don't normally get headaches under any circumstances, so this was bad. I suffer most from nausea, from a sick stomach and a nasty, queasy feeling that precludes eating or drinking. The only answer is sleep, but dread, dread in the pit of my stomach, prevented me. Clogged with phlegm, wanting to throw up, I reached for my cigarettes, only then realising that I didn't recognise the room.

I moved my foot backwards and touched warm flesh. I turned with difficulty. It was Celia.

'Where are we?' I said.

'The Nacional.'

'Do we have any money left?'

'Some.'

'Can we stay here another night? I need to sleep.'

'I think so. Then it is finished. Chris, you fall over in the night. You never do this before.'

'I'm sorry. I won't do it again.

'Chris, no get sick again.'
'Don't worry, I can't afford it now.'

I think crime pays. The hours are good, you travel a lot.
Woody Allen

VERDICT

They all went to trial on the same day. The three killers got life. Of the others only those who'd admitted to anything got prison sentences. In two months José had said nothing. My money may have got the case to trial sooner, that's all. José was on his own. Fifteen to a cell with one pot to piss in. No visitors. Heat and stench. Occasionally a new inmate arrived.

'He would try to speak to me,' said José, 'but I understand. They want me to say something. I never say nothing. Other times I would be taken to the office. "Say something about the others and it will be good for you." I say nothing.'

After two months they gave in. José got a form of probation involving community service.

'Aledmis, he say something,' said José.

Aledmis, his friend from the loft, had talked. He got thirty years. Clearly he had nothing to do with the murder. Maybe he admitted to other things. Maybe the police knew he'd done something else. I didn't know. I remembered his lovely loft space, his skill at chess and thoughtful nature. Thirty years.

'He cry,' said José, without emotion or obvious concern.

The implication being that he should have kept his mouth shut. And he shouldn't have cried. He shrugged. That's life. What about Andy? José said he thought they would shoot him. I disagreed. Andy was not much of a citizen, but he was an all-American citizen. If Fidel could have made political capital out of it he would. The awful Yankees coming to Cuba and murdering tourists. But this had been a drug deal. Drugs were coming through Cuba, if not staying very long. There was no mileage in that, so shooting a US citizen wouldn't be wise. They'd quietly deport him later.

José was a hero in his barrio. He came out thin and grinning with a thick black beard. Girls wanted him and got him. Celia looked on with amusement until they got bored. Then she went back to him.

I asked José what had happened with Andy and Jared.

'The time you see me in the Ambos Mundos with Jared, he ask me where he can buy cocaine. I told him about Andy, that's how he makes his money. Jared gave me his phone number, that's all.'

'And Andy killed him?'

'Andy and two other men. They took his money, $30000. They never had the cocaine.'

'How did the police know?'

'One of them got scared. He was going to speak to the police. They shot him and threw him in a ditch, but he didn't die, the gun was no good.' He shrugged: 'This is Cuba. The man got to a hospital and they called the police. He told them everything.'

His release coincided with my fiftieth birthday. In celebratory mood he threw a party at his expense for both of us. We had gallons of illicit rum served in small jars, lethal, but enjoyable stuff. The party was half in the street, half in what was really just a coffee bar, adapted for the day. Later, he showed me a photo of the party. Of me with Celia. I was sprawled on the sofa, an empty rum bottle at my feet. I had my arm round Celia, whose head was nestled into the crook of my neck, one arm draped across my chest, the other round my waist. Both our heads were back, mouths agape. José laughed,

'You were like this for hours. Both snoring. Very comical.'

Comical, yes, but sort of right too.

I went back to Tony's. I had no choice. I had no money to pay Rosa's rent. I doubted she still wanted to marry me.

The best way to die is sit under a tree, eat lots of bologna and salami, drink a case of beer, then blow up.
Art Donovan

PAUL'S LAST VISIT

Paul had promised to bring funds. He arrived fairly sober, smiling nervously. He waved his shoulder bag at us.

'Wait until you see what I've got in here.'

My heart sank. I turned and walked towards our taxi. José got in the front.

'Don't you want to see?' he said as we set off.

I couldn't speak. He rummaged in the bag and produced some cheque books and cards.

'These will get us anything we want.'

'Cheque guarantee cards?'

'OK. They won't get you cash, but you can buy goods. You can stock up.'

'In England, not here.'

'Why not?'

'Is anything backing them up. Is there any cash anywhere.'

He stared back and said nothing.

'This is Cuba,' I said.

'I know that.'

We travelled in silence for a few minutes.

'I've got around 500 dollars,' he said.

For a week we circled the big hotels, buying only drinks. We bought food at the markets and ate at Tony's. I knew that Paul had funds, thought he'd decided that I was a lost cause. He'd brought just enough to last for the two weeks of his visit. I was morose and sulky while Paul was at his most cheerful. His cheques had worked so far. That was OK provided we had cash to back them up, but the cash was slowly dwindling on supplies for the house.

After a week the cash had almost gone. Paul was unconcerned, confident that the cheques would continue to work. I doubted that, there was always a cut-off point and we were approaching it. On the second Saturday Paul wanted to eat out. Although his money was low, José and I had a few dollars, enough to eat in a peso restaurant, maybe some drinks somewhere else. We took him to Chinatown, cheap and cheerful, but they served good food.

He didn't appear to notice where he was until our food arrived. He stared at it in disgust.

'What the fuck is this?'

'It's your dinner.'

He pushed it away and looked around the bar, caught someone's eye.

'What the fuck are you looking at?' he said.

A well-dressed man of about forty was staring calmly at our table. Not unusual, I thought. People stared everywhere.

'Behave will you?' I said.

José nudged me.

'Eat quickly.'

In the street José said he thought the man was police of some kind.

'You sure?'

'No, but he look like that. That is the way they look at you.'

'Who the fuck cares,' said Paul, 'can we go to the Melia and get some eatable food?'

José and I looked at each other; he shook his head.

'We don't have the money, Paul, I keep telling you.'

'We do have fucking money.'

He flashed the guarantee cards again.

'Put them away,' I said.

I pulled him into a shop. Cuban women were milling around, buying fabrics, towels, toiletries. They looked at the drunken Englishmen, showed brief embarrassment for us, then continued with their business. I pushed him gently to a corner. José stayed by the door, watching the street. I put my hands on his shoulders and stared into his red rimmed eyes.

'Listen to me. The cards are dodgy, they've worked so far, but they might stop working at any time, correct?'

He was angry, shaking with temper beneath my hands.

'Every time we've used them until now we've had the cash to pay if the cards failed. If it failed we could have shrugged and smiled, said "Oh, I am sorry, seem to have reached my limit on that one, have some cash instead." Even if they think we're crooks it doesn't matter. They have their money. They don't care. No harm done. Do you understand?'

He breathed rum fumes into my face, but didn't say anything, his lips a tight sulky line.

'Now,' I said, 'now we don't have the money to cover the prices in the top hotels. We can eat in the peso places. We can still buy gallons of rum. But we can't live the way we have been. We don't have the money. We have to get down and dirty for a while. You only have to put up with it for a few days and then you can go home. I've been living like this for three fucking months. Has it hit home yet? That's why I needed more from you. That's why the *exactly* four hundred dollars you sent for my visas left me high and dry every time. You didn't even get the exchange rate right. You left me short. I had to borrow the rest from Tony.'

The women were staring now. This was more than they'd expected from an early evening trip for essentials. Paul looked back at them, his face red with anger.

'Don't say anything,' I said.

José was trying to look casual in the doorway, he didn't like this. Neither did I. I'd been determined not to get personal, not let my feelings out. Paul would be gone again soon and I still needed him. I had to convince him that the cars were an investment, not wasted money. I took a deep breath.

'We can go get a couple of drinks in the Melia, we can afford that.'

José shook his head at the wasted money.

'OK? Shall we go to the Melia and talk about this?'

He nodded. We left a bunch of disappointed women to their shopping and headed off for a taxi we could barely afford.

We sat in silence for a while nursing our drinks in the lobby. The rich came and went about their business.

'I'm going to use this card,' said Paul.

José and I exchanged a look. How can such a clever man be so stupid?

'You can't,' I said.

'Who dares wins.'

'Who dares gets arrested, Paul. Honestly.'

'I've done this all over the world. I'm not stopping now.'

'And if the card doesn't work?'

'We'll do a runner.'

The lobby was massive. We wouldn't have got as far as the door.

'Run where?'

'Out,' he said,' as though talking to an idiot, 'out there.' He waved his arm vaguely in the direction of what was actually the sea.

'And then?'

'Then we're out. Who dares wins,' he repeated.

'This is Cuba, Paul.'

'I know it's fucking Cuba and I'm fucking pissed off with it.'

A group at the next table stared at us; a woman shook her head and tutted. All three of us glared back at them. They looked away. A couple of the hotel security staff watched us from a distance, speaking occasionally into their short wave radios. José caught my eye, tilted his head in the direction of the door. Let's get out of here.

'OK. We run. We get away from here. Then what?'

'Then that's it, we're out of here.'

'When you leave they will stop you at the airport. Tourism is their livelihood. You do not rip them off. Nobody does. They will stop you and you will pay them. If you're polite they will just deport you and you won't be able to come back. If you behave as you normally do they will lock you up for as long as they please. You should feel right at home.'

'Cunt.'

Paul wouldn't leave. We couldn't abandon him, so we sat, a black cloud of alcohol fumes floating above us. The atmosphere was horrible. Half the hotel was staring at us and most of the security people too. I was worried for José. They would only deport me. Paul got unsteadily to his feet.

'Watch this,' he said.

We watched.

He wobbled in the direction of reception in his too tight swimming shorts. His ankles were swollen with mosquito bites and too much sun. His beer gut strained at his white Viva Fidel t-shirt. He hit some sofas, chairs and tables but kept going, leaning way too far forward, as though the top half of his body wanted to fall over, but his legs weren't going to allow that to happen, and so they scurried along, faster and faster, in an effort to stay upright. He bumped into a few people, half stopped, smiled apologetically in what I'm sure he thought was a charming fashion, but was actually a thin opening on a slightly wild, bright red tomato face. A calamity was staggering towards reception under the impression that he was James Bond after one or two dry martinis, shaken but not stirred, and he was going to show us all how it was done – me, José, Cuba – and we were invited to sit back and watch, watch a true professional at work. This was how it was done. And so we watched. We sank back into the soft sofas and tried to disappear. How had it all come to this? How had it got this silly? This was so *out of control.*

Paul somehow reached reception. He leaned gratefully on the counter and spoke to an attractive female receptionist. She gave him a beautiful smile and listened intently as he spoke. He was there for over half an hour. She scurried back and forth, she made some phone calls and she examined his card. She smiled and she listened and she smiled some more. Eventually he took her hand and kissed it, gave a little bow. She laughed. He started back, but had forgotten where we were. He looked around helplessly. A security man guided him back to our table, nodded politely to each of us in turn. Paul flopped heavily into the cushions and grinned at us.

'There you go boys, that's how it's done.'

He'd managed to buy another round of drinks. The card had stood for it. We could have got them from the bar via a waiter in two minutes. I looked at José. He just seemed relieved that it was over.

'Well done, Paul,' I said.

I patted him on his shoulder. José stood up and patted him too.

'That was good, Paul. How did you do that?'

And he sat down and laughed. We all did.

In the taxi home I said,

'Can we make that the last one, with that card? We can eat at home, watch some TV. We have plenty of booze.'

'Of course. Now I've shown you guys how it's done.'

We stopped at the usual place on the way home. We

bought three litres of Silver Dry and a hundred Hollywood Red cigarettes. I thought it might last us until Paul left. It didn't last us the night.

We watched two movies and then put on some music. A bottle had disappeared and José was as drunk as I'd ever seen him. Paul was laughing at everything, the films, the stories – everything. I needed to talk about the money. I thought he owed me, at least enough to get on my feet again. I tried José, asked him to explain to Paul why buying three cars was a good idea, how it would keep me here, keep Tony happy, start everything going again. I hadn't heard José slur his speech before, or mix his English with Spanish, or talk such utter bollocks. He stood up to demonstrate where we could keep the cars. He swung his arm in an expansive sweep, indicating Tony's drive, then continued in that direction and fell with a loud slap on the tiled floor.

'Hmm,' said Paul, 'can't say I'm convinced.'

José giggled on the floor. I poured another rum and considered my options. Nothing came to mind.

'Why do you want to stay here anyway? It's a shithole. I enjoyed the first visit, novelty value and all that. But you can't get anything done. They just dance and smile and let you down and then forget about everything the next day.'

'Is a shithole,' said José from the floor, 'they forget about everything.'

And he giggled some more.

'Really,' Paul said, 'why do you want to stay here? Come back to England. I'll pay for your ticket.'

'No you won't. You're not even paying for these drinks.

We paid for them.' I gestured vaguely in the direction of José, who was still on the floor.

'I'll send you a ticket when I get back, you'd spend cash if I sent that. You haven't answered my question. Why do you want to stay here?'

'Yamilia,' I said.

'Oh no,' groaned a voice from the floor.

'That fucking bitch,' said Paul.

José managed to get to his hands and knees.

'Chris, Paul, I go to bed.'

'Night, José,' said Paul.

He crawled slowly along the corridor. He wasn't supposed to stay here, one of Tony's rules. I didn't care. And how would he know anyway?

I woke the same day at about 12.00 to a hammering in the corridor. It must be Tony. I didn't want to move, every fibre in my body screamed out for more sleep, for oblivion. The hammering though, whatever it was, served a dual purpose, one of which was to get us up. I didn't care about the other purpose. I staggered into the back bathroom and threw up. A brown female tarantula stared up at me from the floor about a foot away from my face. Just try it, I thought, I'll fucking bite you back, we'll see who's the most poisonous today. From there I made it to the kitchen and drank a litre of water from the fridge. Tony was kneeling in the corridor fiddling with a fan. So that's what the hammering was about. Why is he hitting a fan? I had to face him.

'Buenos dias, Tony. Como esta?'

He looked up at me, sad rather than angry and didn't reply. He rose creakily to his feet, sighed heavily,

'Cafe, Chris?' he said.

I sat in the living room while he made coffee. The floor was littered with cans and bottles. Just one of the litre bottles of rum stood by a chair, maybe a third full, the other two lay on their side on the floor, empty. Beer cans, some squashed, were all over the room. Ashtrays were overturned. The black fan lay on its side in the corridor. It was badly dented and, evidently, no longer functional.

Tony returned with the coffee and handed me a cup. He looked at me and opened the patio door – I must have stank of rum.

'José aqui, Chris?'

I assumed he was, although there was no sign or sound from either of them.

'Si, Tony.'

He shook his head sadly.

'Malo, Chris, muy malo.' This is bad.

He gestured to the fan.

'Que problema el ventilador?'

I didn't know. No idea at all, but it must have had something to do with me, or Paul, or both of us.

'You hit me with it,' said Paul from the corridor.

He made his way unerringly to the remaining rum and poured himself a glass.

'Morning, Tony,' he said.

He showed us the red and blue welt on his shoulder, stretching along the top and down his back. Tony picked up the fan, held it against Paul's shoulder and nodded, mystery solved. He scratched his head and smiled.

'You were aiming for my head,' said Paul, 'you chased

293

me around the garden. There's snakes and every fucking thing out there.'

José had appeared, looking ill. He apologised meekly to Tony, who just nodded and shrugged. He was more interested in the story of the fan now. So was I. José stared at the bruise and Paul explained. Tony cheered up and sat down, grabbed a bottle of water. He looked at Paul's glass and shook his head, in awe, I think.

'You seemed to think I owed you twenty grand because of the Amex card and the disappearing transfer,' he said, as José translated for Tony. 'We had a difference of opinion about that. And you had a certain amount of resentment about the cash for visas and exchange rates. You called me a cunt several times.'

'And I hit you because of that?' I said.

'Not entirely. I called Yamilia a crazy tart, said you were mad for getting involved with her. You went berserk, like a whirling dervish. I had to hide in the street until you gave up and went to sleep.'

José was giggling again and a smile forced itself onto Tony's face. Soon we were all laughing. I poured myself some rum and Tony couldn't be bothered to disapprove.

'Can we get some more booze?' said Paul.

Tony cleaned up. We helped a bit, but we weren't up to much. Paul nursed his rum. When we were done Tony spoke to José and me in the kitchen. He would go out for some food. We needed to eat; he would cook for us. We could have some rum, but we weren't to get drunk. His eyes slid towards Paul in the other room, acknowledging that it might already be too late there. Then he wanted a meeting, the four of us, José could translate. Something had to happen. This situation could not continue. Paul didn't understand the situation, he didn't understand Cuba. We would explain it to him, make a plan, see if we could get everything straightened out. Good idea, Tony.

Tony addressed himself to Paul. He gestured around himself. This is my house, he said. Paul sipped his rum, smiled and waited patiently for Tony to say something he didn't already know. Tony noted the expression, smug, superior and changed his tone slightly. This is my house and it is also my business. I can put tourists here every week, four, six, maybe more can stay here. Twenty-five, thirty dollars each a day. Paul began to pay attention. A possible one thousand dollars weekly, and Tony owned several houses. Paul judged people by appearance. Tony drove an ancient Lada, as did many Cubans. He dressed the same way every day, light chinos and a white shirt that soon became grubby with sweat and food. Paul didn't take him seriously, didn't take any Cubans seriously; they were a fickle, annoying, inferior race – they had their novelty value, especially the women, the white women anyway – but he didn't listen to them, he didn't get it, he didn't know where he was or what was going on. But this was interesting.

Tony listed some ways we could make money. Forget Rumbos and tourism, that's history, there are easier ways. It hadn't gone well so far, mistakes had been made. But I was still here. It was a learning process and it could still work out. Surely Paul would like a contact here? A friend who was secure in a nice house in a country with no extradition treaty, where visitors, as long as they weren't completely stupid could get away with much?

'You are a criminal, Paul,' said Tony, 'not serious, not violent, this could be a safe haven for you.'

'Done,' said Paul, 'if you put it that way. Why not? I'll get right onto it as soon as I'm back in the UK. You'll have funds within a week, two maximum.'

We drank to that.

Do you suppose I could buy back my introduction to you?
Groucho Marx

A Phone Call

I watched through the wooden shutters. He was due soon.
He came every day to check on my health and cook breakfast. Dingo would hear him coming and go crazy, then,
thirty seconds later Tony's car would pull up in front of
the house. As soon as I heard Dingo I sat on the sofa, two
fans moving the hot air around, and tried to look innocent.

'Bueno, Chris,' he said with a broad smile, 'como esta?'

'Bueno, Tony, muy bien.'

We shook hands, a daily ritual. He studied me and
smiled again. He ruffled my hair.

'Ay Chris,' he said laughing and went outside to feed
Dingo.

I stayed put. I'd had another bout of pneumonia, was
convalescing again and not expected to move. Tony had
banned me from drinking, said if he ever found any rum
in the house he'd throw me out. He wouldn't, not while
he still believed I could come up with the sort of money
that had brought us together in the first place, but for now
I was broke and he was making the rules. Also, we'd be-

come friends of a sort, the fact that I was still in his house after several rent-less weeks testified to that. Tony was a businessman first and foremost. I'd become an investment. The question was: how long before he decided it was a bad one and cut his losses? That depended on Paul. Where was Paul? He said two weeks maximum. This was the fourth week and we'd heard nothing.

Dingo was slobbering at his scraps while Tony picked fruit in the garden. He'd juice it in an ancient blender, add about a pound of sugar and hand it to me.

'Bueno para sangre, Chris, fuerte, mucho fuerte.' Good for blood, strong, very strong, and he'd flex his muscles and stick out his chest. We'd both laugh, as we'd done yesterday and the day before that. Tony prepared breakfast and brewed coffee. He always ate with me. He shovelled food into his mouth like a JCB on speed. A few years older than me, his stomach was testimony to a life-long love affair with food. I'd be barely three mouthfuls into my breakfast when he'd finish eating, rest his chin on his big hands and watch me with his sharp green eyes; watching for signs of lack of appetite; lack of appetite brought on by drinking. He thought I was dangerously thin. My appetite was fine. I finished in my own time.

'Bueno, Chris?'

'Very good, Tony. Gracias.'

We talked about nothing for a while, uneasy because we both knew there was only one topic that interested him now, it hung in the air always.

He handed me the pack of ten cigarettes he allowed me each day. I'd hustled five dollars from the Cubans at pool in the local bar the night before, and for a few nights before that. José and I treated ourselves to a half-bottle of rum and a packet of cigarettes each time. He knew most things that went on in Bahia, but not that, I hoped.

'Paul?' he asked.

I shook my head. I didn't have the Spanish to invent an excuse. I told him that I was sure something would happen in the next few days. He shook his head sadly. Paul. The demon alcohol.

'Lentamente, Chris, lentamente, slowly.' Looking me in the eyes. 'La vida. Life. Mucho rapido. No bueno. No good.'

I nodded sagely at this advice. He ruffled my hair again and rose to do the washing-up, laughing as he cleared away the plates.

The phone rang. I hurried to the other room.

'Hello, Paul?'

Silence.

'Is that you, Paul?'

'Is that Mr Hilton?'

A pause.

'Yes.'

'Who do you think you are talking to?'

'Paul?'

'This is Paul Ferguson. Sheffield CID.'

'Yes.'

'And you are Christopher Hilton, previously of Fir Cottage, Leighton Buzzard?'

'Yes.'

'Are you acquainted with a Mr Paul Sant?'

'I know him.'

'He says he knows you too. We have him in custody.

He's been babbling incoherently all night. I don't believe a word he's told us. At one stage he was on about some stuffed birds.'

'So you phoned Cuba?'

'He insisted. He's in a lot of trouble. He says you can confirm his story.'

'Babbling about stuffed birds has got him in trouble?'

'There's rather more to it than that,' he said.

Somehow I thought there would be. Tony put his head round the door, mouthed 'Paul?' at me. I nodded, smiling and gave him the thumbs up. He said 'mas tarde', later, and indicated that he had to go, would phone me tonight. I continued to smile idiotically until I heard the door close.

'Sorry, that was my landlord,' I said.

'So, you have business interests in Cuba?'

'Yes, I live here.'

'Very nice.'

'Yes. It is.'

'What kind of business?'

'Am I in trouble?' I asked.

'Not as far as I know. Are you?

'No. So why should I answer your questions?'

'Because unless you corroborate Mr Sant's story he's not going anywhere. We'll charge him and refuse bail.'

'What is his story?'

'Beyond stuffed birds, I'm not prepared to tell you that.'

'If I don't know what he's told you how can I confirm it?'

'By answering my questions.'

'I need time to think about this.'

'You don't have any.'

'Hang on a moment, my landlord wants to speak to me.'

I put the phone on the table, lit a cigarette and went into the garden. Right. I'm in Cuba, they're not. Even if they know something they can't do anything because there's no extradition treaty. What has Paul told them? Don't know. Doesn't matter. I'm here. They're there. Nothing to lose. If they do have Paul. They must do. Stuffed birds? Why did he tell them that? He must have been paralytic. OK. Tough it out.

'Hello, sorry about that.' I said.

'Well?'

'What do you want to know?'

'Did you give Mr Sant permission to use your credit cards?'

'Yes.'

'Generous man.'

'That's the kind of guy I am.'

'Including a platinum Amex card.'

'Yes.'

'You are generous.'

'Thank you.'

'Did you know that Mr Sant has run up a bill of £28000 on your Amex card?'

'Yes.'

Bastard.

I see,' he said. 'Why?'

'Why what?'

'Why did you give him permission to use it?'

'I have a business in Cuba. I need a representative in England. Transferring money to and from Cuba is difficult. Hence the cards.'

'What kind of business?'

'Tourism.'

'That would be Eternity Travel.'

'Yes.'

He laughed.

'It figures. Apparently Mr Sant is a director of the company.'

'Yes.'

'And you're not?'

'No.'

'I see.'

What did he see?

'And John Freedman is also a director?'

'I don't know. I don't know how the business was set up.'

'And was Michelle Lewis the signed witness to a £40000 secured loan on a property in Leighton Buzzard?'

'I'm not answering that.'

'Then Mr Sant stays in his cell.'

'She has nothing to do with this.'

'We need to confirm that she was a signatory.'

'How?'

'Tell us how we can contact her.'

'I don't know.'

'We just need to confirm Mr Sant's story, nothing more. A phone call would be enough.'

'I need to think about this. Give me half an hour.'

'No. I'll give you ten minutes. I'll call back. If you don't cooperate Mr Sant stays where he is.'

He hung up.

I paced the garden, smoking. Dingo watched me, his

head tilted to one side, emitting occasional little yelps, as if to say: 'Now what? Now what have you done.' He saved my life once. I didn't think he could help with this. Not unless they came to the house to get me. Then he'd help. Right. Slow down. You're being irrational. You haven't done anything illegal. A bit naughty maybe, but not illegal. Not in England anyway. What Paul might have done is his business. What did he do? How did he get himself arrested? I'll ask. Right. Michelle. She doesn't know she was a signatory. She soon will. Shit. Doesn't matter. She's done nothing wrong. If I don't tell them they'll get there sooner or later and that could be worse. I'm going to have to tell them. I'll phone Michelle before they get to her. Right. OK. I must have been talking out loud because Dingo let out a loud bark of irritation. 'Don't worry,' I said to him as I walked back into the house, 'it must have been that last bang on the head.'

The phone rang.
    'Mr Hilton.'
    'Yes.
    'Paul Ferguson here.'
    'I know.'
    'Why was Paul arrested?'
    'He was at a Sheffield hotel, with an escort.'
    'If you arrested everybody for that half the country would be locked up.'
    'He didn't have any money.'
    'You said he had…'
    'He didn't have any cash, so he called a taxi to take him to an ATM.'

'And?'

'Then he wanted some cigarettes. The taxi driver took him to a garage.'

'Still don't see why he was arrested.'

'According to Mr Sant, when he left the garage he forgot all about the taxi and walked back to the hotel.'

'And the taxi driver called the police,' I said.

'Yes. Actually, that's the only part of his story I believe. Considering the condition he's in, his behaviour makes perfect sense.'

Very funny.

'So,' he said, 'have you made a decision?'

'I'll give you her work phone number. You will be discreet?'

'We will. A female colleague will make the call.'

I gave him the number.

'Mr Hilton?'

'Yes?'

'The stuffed birds?'

'Ten years ago a friend of mine moved to Chicago. He left some of his things with me, including some stuffed birds. He's an ornithologist. They're still in my garage.'

'So it's true,' he said.

'Yes.'

'But why did he keep going on about it?'

'I've no idea. He must have thought it proved something. I think he thought they might be valuable.'

'Are they?'

'No.'

'Incredible.'

'Yes.'

'Well. Goodbye, Mr Hilton. Nice talking to you.'

Incredible.

An hour later José arrived. He hitched out from Havana every day. It could take hours. He took off his sweat-soaked shirt and hung it over a chair in front of one of the fans. I was watching TV. He asked if Paul had phoned.

'No,' I said. 'The police did.'

I told him the story. He thought about it for a while then put his head back and laughed. I laughed with him.

'Fucking Paul,' he said. 'Will he get out?'

'I don't know. Probably. But there's no chance of any money for a while.'

'Shit.' He laughed again. 'If we get out of this we will be heroes.'

Something like that.

We are all as God made us, and many of us much worse.
Narrator: Tom Jones

A NEW ENEMY

I heard nothing from Paul, had no idea if he was in or out. More weeks passed; the hottest, most humid weather arrived and stuck to me, heavy and exhausting. I fought against depression, finding it hard to lift my mood, to find signs of hope in my situation. The morning journey to buy bread left me drenched in sweat and exhausted. There was no air to breathe. The potholed streets, the noise, every breath a struggle; clouds of dust circled, disturbed by every passing car; it lay everywhere: on the leaves of the trees, the parked cars and the shop windows. The hurricane season would wash it all away, clear the air and bring new life but for now all was lifeless, cloying – hopeless. I didn't have the energy to raise a smile at the bakers, was surly and impatient, just wanting to get back in the shade, watch TV, reread a book – shut everything out.

José visited every day now. Sometimes Celia came too, but not often; she was always much quieter around him, perhaps inhibited because she couldn't speak freely. On one of her visits she looked around Tony's house, the empty fridge, the plate of rice and beans he'd left for me and the few cigarettes I had left.

'Chris, how can you live like this?'

'Celia, I don't have any choice.'

She nodded slowly, as though it had only just occurred to her. When José went to the shop for cigarettes she said,

'Come to the flat on Monday. José will be in Guantanamo for a few days.'

When they left I picked up the book I'd been reading, reading for the second or third time. I read and reread the books I had accumulated, rarely watching TV except for Fridays and Saturdays, which were movie nights when current films, presumably taken from a Florida satellite, were shown. If I could manage a few pesos for a quarter bottle of rum, this became a weekend treat, as enjoyable as anything I'd done when money was unimportant.

The book was given to me by Manolo. It was about a Rabbi detective in New York, one of a series of straight-forward whodunits. I can't remember the title. It was a bit silly, but interesting and intriguing enough to pass the time. I got to the last page and noticed something written on the inside back cover that I'd missed before:

'For translation services: $500.'

I tried to remember when Manolo gave me the book. It was many months before, certainly. So he'd been nursing resentment for all this time. Tony had told me not to worry about him. I didn't think of his translation as a service, just something he did when Tony needed him. I thought of him as Tony's gofer, not mine. Manolo clearly thought differently. Well, it was too late now. I couldn't even of-fer fifty pesos, nor would I if I had it. The message left me vaguely disturbed though, and I read it several times before putting the book away and starting a new one.

I kept an increasingly manic diary, full of plans and solutions to my predicament. I had to believe I could get myself out of this. Although I hoped Paul would come through with some money, I never really believed he would. Now that he'd been arrested it seemed stupid even to hope. But hope I did. The contrast between the feelings of freedom and power of my early days here and my present reality were hard to bear or even acknowledge. A certain amount of self-deception was necessary just to get through the day. Tony was losing faith and patience. The faith José and Celia still had was essential. If I lost that...

One night a movie was interrupted by a massive storm, ending reception, so I read instead, my back sweating against Tony's plastic furniture. I felt a light caress on my shoulder and brushed at it. My fingers entwined with thick bristly legs, lots of them. I leapt to my feet as the large, black male tarantula scurried to escape – bad weather tended to bring them in from the garden. I like tarantulas and often shared my shower as one, usually female, watched from the corner of the stall. The females are more dangerous, the males much bigger, black as opposed to her brown, but for those few moments my skin crawled with an illogical panic and I took off my sandal and smashed it to pieces, legs flying everywhere.

I didn't sleep much. Sleep only took me when I was exhausted and lasted two or three hours at most. When I did finally sleep it was usually getting light, neighbours were stirring and traffic noise beginning to rumble in the street. A fan directed at the bed kept hovering mosquitoes at bay. I watched them for hours, diving and forced back, diving and forced back, constantly frustrated. During power cuts I got up and sat in the garden.

José once told me he had five thousand dollars saved, painstakingly hustled over years of trudging the streets of Havana. It was for when he got permission to travel to the US. If he ever got permission. He didn't want to stay there, just earn enough to come back and live comfortably in Cuba. Like many of the young he was slightly schizo-phrenic about Cuba, expressing hatred and resentment for the system, but fiercely proud of it in other ways. I once asked him what he would do if the US invaded.

'We don't want them,' he said. 'We would fight them.'

On Monday I went to see Celia. I left early, before the worst of the heat and stood in the queue of Cubans waiting on the slip road to the motorway. A taxi driver recognised me and stopped. I put my head through the window.

'I don't have any money.'

He laughed.

'I know. I heard. No problem, get in.'

Celia opened a new bottle of rum when I arrived. We watched the street from the balcony for a while and let the rum do its work. She took a healthy gulp from her glass and disappeared. A few minutes later she called me in. She knelt in the middle of the floor, a cardboard shoebox at her knees, secured with elastic bands. She released the lid and tipped the contents onto the floor. A pile of notes spread between us. Her dress rode up to the top of her thighs as she leaned back, supporting herself with her hands on the floor behind her.

'Look here, not there,' she said, pointing at the money. 'This will improve your life.'

It was a big pile, mainly ones and fives, a few tens here and there. It wasn't much, a few hundred dollars, but that wasn't the point.

'Where did it come from?'

She shrugged

'It's mine. Now it's yours.'

'What about José?'

'He has money.'

'Thank you.'

'No. Not thank you. Before you buy everything. All drinks, cigarettes, food, every dance, all the music, all the time. You pay. Not thanks for me, thank you. Now I help you. Finish.'

The last word shouted with a slap of her hands.

'Celia. I need some books.'

'Books?'

She said this as though I'd asked for a new dress.

'Yes. All that time at Tony's. You said you didn't know how I could live like that. Well, I like to read. It makes my time more pleasant, happy.'

'Like Salome?'

'Yes. I can get them from the market. Old books. They don't cost very much.'

'OK. I come with you. You will pay too much.'

I went back to the stall where the guy had sold me the ancient copy of *Plutarch's Lives*. He recognised me immediately.

'Ah, my classical friend. What would you like today? I see you have a new girlfriend.'

I chose a couple of thick Len Deighton paperbacks. Celia knocked him down to nothing, which annoyed him. I stayed with her until José returned. Her gentle companionship, her touch, revived me. Black moods can be beaten.

Mr Kane was a man who got everything he wanted and then lost it.
Citizen Kane

RITA

The local bar provided rum, hamburgers, pizzas and a pool table. On the occasions that I had a few dollars or won at pool, I bought a quarter or half of rum at the counter of the small shop attached to the bar. Rita, who served there, progressed from grumpy practicality to smiles and then outright curiosity. One day she demanded my passport before she would allow me the rum, supposedly for the meticulous records kept of every transaction. She studied my passport, enjoying her authority. At my date of birth she smiled and nodded. If this meant it had corresponded with her guess, higher or lower, I couldn't tell. I told her that I stayed at Tony's house, explaining who and where he was. She cut me off; she already knew. She knew my story. She just didn't know me.

I became a regular, often with José, buying rum as we played pool or to take away. She made no secret of her distaste for strong alcohol, giving us disapproving glares and haughty superior service along with the bottles she slapped onto the counter. She was a busty, voluptuous natural blonde, an unusual combination for Cuba. She always wore tiny denim shorts and skimpy vests, not in showy manner, but because it was always hot in the un-air-conditioned bar. Serious and a bit severe in manner, she changed when she smiled, losing years with a facial movement. She began to watch the pool games, sometimes singles, sometimes me with José against the locals, until they refused to play us anymore. She seemed baffled by the pursuits and interests of men, the pool, the sport and particularly the drinking, and watched with almost pained confusion as to what the fuss and noise was about.

As we sat waiting our turn at pool one night, a soggy note appeared on our table. The handwriting was uneven and childish. José tried to decipher it. He said that it was signed in Rita's name.

'But she didn't write this,' he said.

'Why, what does it say?'

'It is supposed to be a love letter, but it is terrible, the grammar, the spelling. It is impossible that a Cuban person wrote this.'

It hurt his pride that even one Cuban could be illiterate, even in a lowly working man's bar such as this. Then he laughed as he caught someone's eye.

'Now I understand.'

We were joined by the local drunk, ruined by rum but harmless and funny. He had written the note as a joke. He shoved his unshaven face close to mine and breathed fumes over me as he explained, completely unintelligibly, before laughing, slapping me on the back and staggering away.

'What was that about?' I said.

'He says that Rita likes you. He was playing a joke on you by writing the note.'

'Do you think she likes me?'

'I don't know.'

'You think she'd like to come out with me for a night in Havana?'

'Ask her.'

'I don't have enough money.'

'Ask her first. We will find some if she says yes.'

She said yes.

José arranged an unofficial, cheap taxi to Havana, an ancient Chrysler that roared and rumbled its slow way along the motorway, blaring music that couldn't quite drown out the arthritic engine, as we sat in the back, slightly uneasy with each other, on opposite sides of the sumptuous, worn leather seats. I didn't have much money or any idea where I was going to take her. The taxi dropped us by the Ambos Mundos, where Jorgé, catching some late evening sun, called to me from the doorway. We went in for a drink.

She hadn't been to Havana for over two years, seemed less familiar with it than me and had never seen the inside of a hotel. I was acutely aware of the restrictions ordinary Cubans had to suffer, not allowed in to their own hotels and clubs or on to their own beaches or into their own clubs – not without someone like me to accompany them – someone like me who was broke. We looked at the photos of Hemingway in the lobby. I explained that he had written one of his most famous books here, in between visits to the docks to find his women. I watched for her reaction to that, but she just laughed and studied the photographs again. The lobby was fairly empty, the piano, absent of tourist requests, played classical music. Cubans and tourists mingled as they passed the windows of the lobby on two sides. She sipped her Cuba Libre and seemed happy to watch. I desperately tried to drink my mojito at the same slow speed as her. George asked us if we would like to eat at the rooftop bar. She watched my response as I said I wasn't sure, maybe.

I wanted to drink faster because I felt uneasy. If she'd been more talkative or demonstrative I'd have been OK, but although she smiled a lot and seemed happy in my company, I couldn't read her. She wore a light cotton dress. Her hair, as always, was pinned up and she wore minimal make-up, perhaps a little more attention to the eyes, which seemed to be observing me with some amusement. Shorn of my image as irresponsible man about town I wasn't quite sure how to behave. Though she was in her thirties there was still a large age gap. It didn't usually bother me, but now I was surprised that I was even thinking about it. I was tongue-tied.

'You look very beautiful tonight,' I heard myself say.

She laughed as though I'd just cracked a joke and put a hand over mine, rubbing it as if trying to warm it:

'Thank you,' she said, 'don't worry. I'm happy.'

She finished her drink, which gave me the opportunity to regroup while I ordered some more. Jorgé, with nothing to do, came behind the bar to serve me.

'Your new girlfriend?' he said.

'I don't know.'

His moustache twitched.

'Why don't you take her to the roof garden to eat. You can impress her there.'

'I can't. I don't have enough money.'

He put down the two drinks he was mixing and leaned his hands on the bar. He blinked in time with the twitch of his moustache.

'Your money is finished?'

'Yes. I have some, but not much.'

I had fifty of the dollars that Celia had given me. It wasn't enough for the whole evening if we ate at the rooftop restaurant.

'What will you do?'

'I don't know. Go to England, I suppose, and get some more.'

'Can you do that?'

'I think so. I have to.'

He nodded thoughtfully at that and went back to mixing the drinks. He pursed his lips, took a deep breath and exhaled slowly, noisily. He finished the drinks, but left them where they were on the bench in front of him. He looked around the lobby; the piano player had gone, his two colleagues stood at the door chatting. He gave me a long stare, looking right into me as though I were a painting he couldn't quite get, wasn't sure if it was fake or not. I looked away, took some notes from my back pocket.

'Put your money away,' he said, 'pay me the next time you come in. Then you can take her to the roof garden. I will take care of your drinks.'

'I don't know when that will be.'

He looked over at Rosa, who was watching us.

'You will be back. It's only rum.'

He turned away from me and began washing glasses.

We ate on the lovely roof terrace. It had been hot downstairs, but up here there was a cool breeze from the sea. We walked to the stone parapet surrounding the terrace, leaned over and watched the street, dark now, voices and music rose up from the bars below. I watched her face as she gazed out at the lights of the city. She was smiling. I gave up on conversation. She just didn't talk much. I rarely saw her speak to the locals in the bar. She lived alone. She was a loner, like me. Before we sat down again she took my hand.

I stayed at her house most nights after she finished work and she cooked for us on her free days. She had a little English and I worked hard on my Spanish, but we hardly talked at all, she didn't seem to need it. She revealed nothing about her past, smiles and shrugs indicating that it was history and unimportant. She was completely unimpressed with my experiences, merely shaking her head at the incredible waste of money. I drank moderately, partly through necessity and partly to gain her respect, not spoil things.

If she worked during the day I went to see her as soon as Tony left the house. She stopped charging me for my rum and cigarettes, which was risky, and I responded by not drinking and smoking so much. I also got the odd pizza if she could get away with it. As I walked home one afternoon some clods of earth and stones bounced around me and hit my legs with some force. Someone shouted,

'Maricon.'

I looked up as an open truck passed with several people in the back. A young boy stood at the back throwing anything he could find at me, gesticulating and shouting 'Maricon', queer. Someone stood next to him, arms folded, watching calmly. It was Manolo.

I wondered why, now that I was down and out, Rosa had any interest in me. She didn't appear to expect much, perhaps knowing I would be temporary. There were no signs in her house of previous men: photos of husbands, children, relatives, just one picture of her mother. As we ate one night she said she was going to visit her mother in Holguin; that she would be back in two weeks. I never saw her again.

Me that 'ave been what I've been
Me that 'ave gone where I've gone
Me that 'ave seen what I've seen
'Ow can I ever take on
With awful old England again.
Rudyard Kipling

ENOUGH

That night, as I walked home from Rita's, I heard shuffling and giggling behind me. I turned to see Amado, Manolo and the young stone-thrower walking fast towards me. Amado had a knife, a nasty looking old plastic-handled thing, long and so often sharpened I could see the mauve and purple shades of the metal where it had been ground and the thin, chipped sharp edge, gleaming silver at its point. He'd wrapped different coloured tapes around the handle. They stopped in front of me.

Manolo stood leaning against a fence, one knee drawn up, relaxed and indifferent. The young boy, who seemed retarded, bobbed around on his trainers, giggling and watching Amado with wild eyes. Amado held the point to my stomach and pushed slightly as he spat insults at me. I felt it, but it didn't hurt. They're not going to hurt me badly, I thought; they can't. I looked at Manolo. He was too smart for this. He knew what the consequences would be, from the police and from Tony. He could think ahead, unlike the other two. This was an exercise in humiliation.

Amado held the edge of the knife against my throat. He jutted out his chin, comically I thought, and hissed at me through gritted white teeth. There wasn't pressure enough to hurt me, let alone cut me. Manolo watched; he could see that I'd figured this out, the fear they wanted wasn't there. I put a hand in my back pocket where there were a couple of dollars Rita had given me for coffee. Amado moved the knife to the right side of my neck, sliced lightly and jumped away, watching my hand. I pulled out the dollars, crumpled them up and threw them at Manolo,

'Thank you for your translations, Manolo. They were very useful, you're a useful guy.'

He pushed himself away from the fence with his raised foot and rushed at me. I'd never seen him move so fast. His face was contorted as he tried to kick me between the legs. He missed his target and caught me in the stomach, hard enough for me to fall down. The meal and the rum spewed out of my mouth. It was acid, foul, awful. I lay there, the breath gone out of me, and this stuff, still somehow ejecting itself from my stomach. The sight of me made them back off. I was sure they didn't intend to kill me. Amado, needing the last word, aimed a kick at my hip – no, they didn't want to kill me. Well, they *wanted* to, but they were too scared to do it.

They walked away, talking too loudly and laughing. The young boy danced around them in excitement. Amado got off one more 'maricon' before they were out of earshot. I lay there taking in the stench of my vomit, my breath coming slowly back to me. I felt no pain. I walked home trying to take deep breaths from the airless night. At Tony's I checked myself in the bathroom mirror. A tiny cut on my neck had bled onto my t-shirt. A black bruise was appearing on my right side.

I sat on the sofa and vomited over the floor. The tiny black insects that lived in Tony's house, attacking any crumbs or dead insects en masse, converged upon the mess from all sides. 'They are crazy,' José had said, and they looked crazy now as they fed on the pool of vomit. I cleaned my teeth and walked to the kitchen. A quarter of Silver Dry was hidden behind the fridge. Rita had given it to me earlier in the day. I placed it in the freezer and went out to talk to Dingo, who was barking. I fed him some old bread and let him off his chain. He usually shot off round the garden, but he just ambled over to the patio door and lay down. He never tried to enter the house. I got a brush and swept the vomit onto the patio. I'd intended to sweep it into the garden, but Dingo leapt up and devoured it. I took the Silver Dry from the freezer, poured it into a glass and sat back down in the living room. Tony's ancient TV gave me the usual electric shock as I switched it on. I took a sip of rum, my hands began to shake and I felt terribly hot. I retched again, but nothing would come. I could smell my own horrible breath. I felt dizzy, rolled onto the floor and lay on my side, a cheek to the cool tiles. Dingo watched, his head on his front paws, making small whimpering and barking noises.

The static of the TV woke me. It was 8.00 and Tony would be here within the hour. Dingo had taken himself back to his chain. I tied him up. The tiny insects were all over me. I scratched my head and hundreds of them tumbled out. I showered them all away and shaved. Then I cleaned up the house and mopped where I'd been sick.

My ex-wife had phoned me two weeks before. I hadn't contacted anyone in England after I'd run out of money because I couldn't afford to and I didn't want them to worry. I asked Paul to tell a few people that I was OK, that I'd be in touch soon. It turned out he hadn't told anybody anything and they were all worried that I was dead. Anyway, Liz had tracked me down. She said she'd left an open one-way ticket if I needed it, Heathrow via Madrid. A friend had phoned soon after that. If I came back I could stay at their new place in the country, chill out for a while, just in case anybody was looking for me.

I didn't have any coffee. I'd thrown my last two dollars at Manolo. I poured what was left of the rum, a full shot glass. In the bedroom I rummaged everywhere and found two diazepam. I knocked them both back with the rum, cleaned my teeth twice. Tony arrived a few minutes later. He slouched through the house and fed Dingo. He'd brought some coffee with him, just enough for two, in a plastic bag. He was sullen as we drank, letting me know again how I was imposing on his hospitality. I enjoyed the coffee, feeling the caffeine mix nicely with the rum and the diazepam.

'I'm going home, Tony,' I said.

He stared at me, not understanding, but recognising something in my voice.

'To Inglaterre.'

I told him about the ticket. I said I would go to England for three weeks, see Paul, get some money and come back. I had no idea if it was possible. He beamed and shook my hand, said what a good idea it was. When I returned we could start the business and not have to rely on Paul. He found a bottle he'd hidden somewhere, and poured us both a generous glass. And then another. He was in a good mood, like old times, he could smell money again. Even if I didn't make it he could rent his house now. He wanted me to make it though. He left happily two hours later. He didn't want to clash with José, who he knew would be over soon.

With the extra rum I felt great. With diazepam, if you don't lie down and sleep immediately, they wake you up; make you think that everything is fine, or at least not terrible. I didn't tell Tony that twenty minutes before he arrived, before the rum and diazepam, that I'd been shaking badly; that I'd had nausea and fear in the pit of my stomach I could barely stand, that I didn't know what to do anymore, where to go, what to say, how I would eat – how I would I stay alive; that my head span with the confusion of it all. I'd had enough.

And yet her name was like a summons to all my foolish blood.
James Joyce: Araby

FINDING YAMILIA

We sat outside a restaurant near The Capitolio. We'd eaten and were passing the afternoon with a bottle of rum, watching the teeming crowds, all the chaos of everyday life in Havana. I was down, so José was down – that's the way it worked with us. He fed off my moods and desires, but was always there. I felt Cuban now. I didn't want to go home, was determined to come back. Whatever it was about Cuba, it suited me. I was at home here, comfortable with all it could throw at me, but I couldn't survive here without money. Not without doing things I wasn't prepared to do.

'I want to see Yamilia,' I said.

José shook his head. I hadn't seen her in many months, had no idea what she was doing. He tried to get out of it, said she probably wasn't in Havana, that she wouldn't want to see me and that we wouldn't be able to find her.

'I want to see her before I leave. In case I don't come back.'

'You will come back.'

'In case I don't.'

He had no choice. I handed him my cellular. He began calling people. I cheered up at the idea of seeing her, began to see more life and happiness in the streets. Thirty minutes later he gave me back the phone.

'What?' I said. 'Did you find her?'

'I know where to find her.'

'Where is she?'

'She is working.'

'Working? Yamilia?'

'In a shop,' he said, 'she is working and staying with her relatives.'

'I don't believe it.'

'I know where the shop is. You want to go and look?'

'Yes,' I said, 'let's go and look.'

We walked to the shop, about a mile away. It was a convenience peso store, some food items, some clothing, some electrical goods. A bit of everything and not much of anything. Big, old-fashioned and under-stocked, like hundreds of others. I couldn't see her. José spoke to someone.

'She's not here,' he said, 'she works alternate days' – the miracle of full employment – 'this is one of her days off.'

'But she does work here?'

'They say she does. I have her number.'

I gave him the cellular.

'Call her.'

'What shall I say?'

Good question.

We walked to the Ambos Mundos. We decided on what now seems like a pretty silly plan. José would call her and say he wanted to meet her about something important. They would meet in the lobby of the Ambos Mundos, while I waited across the street in a bar. Later he would suggest another place and he'd bring her to me. A big surprise.

The bar was full of tourists and some Cubans who'd latched onto them. I watched an intense European couple listening, starry eyed, as a version of José extolled the virtues of the revolution, the absolute perfectness of life under Fidel. And could they just manage twenty dollars for some new shoes? The embargo, you know. The wicked Americans. I felt like an old hand, the cynical old-timer in the corner – and even sadder about leaving.

Yamilia had finally found trouble with Lazaro and Amado. In the end they got nothing and they blamed her. She was on her own again. She walked in as though the place belonged to her. She saw me immediately, smiled a knowing smile, stopped ten feet away and said loudly, completely without concern for the room full of tourists:

'Who dance like this? What man dance like this?'

She began to dance with an exaggerated swinging of the arms and clumsy foot movements. Everyone in the bar was watching her. She didn't take any notice of them, just continued with her dance, making me love her again instantly and saying, in her way, that the meeting was OK, that she was pleased to see me, that she remembered the dancing, that even I didn't dance that badly. She sat down. Her eyes bore through me. She picked up the menu and ordered a beer.

'How are you? You married? You have babies yet?'

'It's only been a few months.'

She shrugged. Months, years, decades – what was the difference? Time was liquid in Cuba. She had no idea how long it had been. She didn't care.

There was a smile in her eyes, showing me that her life went on the same no matter what. It wasn't an act. It was the way things were, the way things were with her. She was lean. She'd never been overweight, but at the height of our high living she'd put on a few pounds. She looked great. She looked better off without me. She gave me a long once over.

'Your eyes are tired.'

She looked at some fresh grazes on my arm, the result of a night out with José when, with Celia's money, we'd bounced off a few walls, fallen into a few gutters. She shook her head. That sort of thing didn't happen when she was around. José wasn't around when she was around.

She picked up my mobile, called one of her friends. She chatted for a few minutes. I could tell it was another woman, maybe one of her cousins. She saw me watching her.

'How much you spend calling Paul?'

Her logic was flawless, but my phone was nearly empty. I let her finish. I knew she'd stop in a few minutes. This was a game.

We finished our drinks and walked to a peso place. We sat at the bar, facing each other on high stools. José sat behind her, facing in the other direction. Sometimes he'd listen to us, but most of the time he watched the games of pool, chatted to others.

She told me about her job in the shop. She got eight dollars a week, a good wage. With enthusiasm she said that at the end of the week she could get goods from the shop for free, and much cheaper at any time. I thought she was genuine. I was happy that she was happy. I also knew that this was a novelty that would soon wear off. She'd met José tonight hoping for an angle. Eight dollars a week and cheap food wasn't going to keep Yamilia in nice clothes from dollar shops. José looked at me over her shoulder, shaking his head in amusement. I didn't care. When she was happy, I was happy. I told her I was leaving on Friday. That I was out of money and had to go home to make some more. I'd be back in two or three weeks.

'You can go to England?' she said.

'Why not?'

'You don't have trouble with the police?'

'No. Why?'

'Rosa said you could not go home for two years or you would have trouble with the police.'

'Rosa. What does she know?'

'You are not a criminal?'

'No.'

She lowered her head, looked at me from under her lashes.

'I think you poco criminal, Chris.'

'Poco. Maybe.'

'Tony said you were washing money.'

'Tony said that? When?'

'Back then,' she said. 'When everything was crazy.'

When everything was crazy. The relationship was difficult for her. When we were away from Havana we got

328

on OK, we were happy. In Camaguey. In Pinar Del Rio. In Matanzas. In Guanabacoa at the beginning. When everything was crazy. When the house was quiet, we got on OK. We did. You drank too much. I did. Paul was crazy. He was. I didn't want much. You didn't. I cooked and cleaned for you. Not really, you got someone else to do it, but I admired that. I look after you when you sick. You did. I gave you good love. You did. She took my hand gently. Not like Yamilia. She put it between her legs, clamped them shut. Very like Yamilia.

'I loved you.'

'No, you didn't.'

'You think I don't love you? I take you here, here and here.'

She pointed between her legs, her mouth, behind her. You think I don't love you? You think I do this for anybody? You think I do for money? I live with you, cook for you, clean for you. I look after you when you sick. Me happy with you. Too many people. José. Tony. Too many people. Everything was crazy.'

It was.

'What you want, Chris?'

I don't know. Everything?

The barman was watching us. He raised his eyebrows at me, shook his hand as though it was burning. She didn't notice. She rarely noticed, or cared about other stuff. It was no concern of hers. What other people thought was their problem.

'Me no crazy,' she said.

And I thought: were you crazy? I remember the other times. When you flew at people for some imagined offence.

Your moments of generosity followed by moments of extreme cruelty. The time in the hospital when you pretended your leg was hurt and you had them all running around after you like a prima donna. At the expense of all those people who really needed help. When you screamed at José and me in a roadside bar that night. You screamed at us with two old Cubans watching. You paced around just screaming at us. You kicked over tables and chairs. You broke glasses and bottles. And... and you're right. Without the others we might have been happy still. And I love you more than ever.

'You come back?'

'Yes.'

'You sure?'

'Yes.'

'OK. Let's go.'

We walked fifty yards up Obispo. She stopped and shouted up to a window. A middle-aged woman appeared on the balcony. A casa particular. José stayed in the bar. We waited while the woman made a room ready. Before everything went bad at the Blue House, Yamilia had tried to get pregnant. It was her theory that the more excited she got me, the more potent I would be. She would play with me for an hour before letting me inside her.

'Now you have much juice, much power here.'

She went to work again now, determined and methodical. Talking all the time, what she was going to do to me, what she wanted me to do to her. I came inside her quickly, but she wouldn't allow me to stop. With her legs wrapped around my neck she urged me on, slapping my backside hard, pushing me deeper. When I came a second time she relaxed. Whatever I had left would be too weak to make anything.

'In fifteen year, when you old man in Havana, there will be a beautiful girl here with green eyes. Every man wants her. You will follow her everywhere to stop the men from having her because she is yours and you love her. You will be so jealous and angry with the men. You will want to kill them.'

'What if it's a boy?'

'He will fuck every woman in Havana.'

The woman banged on the door. Time to go.

I walked her to top of Obispo. One of a crowd of boys said something as we passed. They all laughed, so did Yamilia.

'What did they say?'

'They say that to kiss me you have to put me on a box.'

It was 4.00 a.m.

'I have to work in four hours,' she said.

I kissed her on the forehead. The boys laughed and shouted. I lifted her up and kissed her on the lips. They cheered.

'I'll see you in two weeks.'

'OK.'

José and I got a taxi. After dropping him off in Havana it took me to Bahia and Tony's. I fell into bed, happy for the first time in months.

The next day I realised I didn't have my phone with me. I wanted it in case Yamilia phoned. José turned up at 3.00. He had it.

'Yamilia has phoned, maybe ten times,' he said.

'What did she say?'

'She wanted to talk to you.'

I called the number she'd been ringing from. It was a communal phone, shared between one floor of a tenement. A woman answered in rapid, bad-tempered Spanish. I passed the phone to Jose.

'She isn't there,' he said.

'Why didn't you give me the phone back last night?'

'We were drunk,' he said. 'I forgot.'

Am I ever going to see your face again? (No way, get fucked, fuck off!)
The Angels, song title

LEAVING

I gave up on Paul, no longer waiting by the phone or checking at the bank for funds. The knee I'd injured in the accident began to fail and I found the long walk to the bank too much of a struggle, with only bad news at the end of it. Raul advised me to get x-rays in England, where they had better equipment.

I wanted to stay. I considered asking Yamilia if we could live in Lugareno, but despite her previous assurances I didn't think she could live without money. I knew that I couldn't. So I waited at Tony's house for the day of my departure. Rita was still in Holguin; I had no way of contacting her to tell her I was leaving. José and Celia arrived every afternoon and stayed late into the evening. Afterwards I hardly slept, reading or writing in my diary through the night. Sometimes I sat in the garden watching the neighbourhood come to life.

I didn't really like Tony's house. It didn't suit me, was too hot and lacking the breezes I was used to in Villa Pan Americana and Havana. But I would have stayed if I could.

I would have stayed anywhere. The strength of my attachment, even in such circumstances, surprised me. Cuba gets a bad press and most people believe what they read without question. I'm not blind to Cuba's bad points, which are many, but I find the hatred of Castro baffling. Media commentators queue up to criticise Cuba for a multitude of sins. Why? Why is it so important to them? The nasty little dictatorships of Central and South America, torturing and killing to protect US business interests, don't appear to concern them. Is that what they want for Cuba? Exactly what they had before they threw the Americans out? Is it the idea of Cuba that so concerns them, the idea of an alternative to mass greed? OK, the idea hasn't worked, but it tried, and in many ways is still trying. And without the crippling fifty-year embargo – who knows? Perhaps that is the cause of the hostility, the fact that the *idea* is still alive somewhere, threatening the size of their pools, cars and fridges, the possibility that instead of owning ninety per cent of the world's riches, they might have to make do with eighty.

I told Tony I'd see him in two weeks. José and Celia came to the airport with me. I checked in, Heathrow via Madrid. We had a few hours to kill and enough money for food and rum. I wanted to buy some presents for them, but money was far too low. More in hope than expectation I wondered down to an ATM. Five minutes later I was back. I threw eight hundred dollars onto the table. Celia looked around nervously.

'Paul,' I said. 'He sent five thousand.'

José shook his head slowly. Celia did her disappearing

act. Five thousand at any time in the last three months would have got us started again.

'Fucking Paul,' he said.

I bought them presents and gave them some money. I left José something for Yamilia.

'Will you give it to her?'

'I'll give it to her.'

'No, I mean, will you give it to her?'

He nodded. I looked at Celia who nodded too. Could she make him? I hoped so.

At the gate I turned to wave. I felt fine, a bit choked maybe, but I didn't think this was goodbye. I upgraded to first class. I knew the security procedure by heart. I didn't think they would stop me leaving. Sure, there were a few security people curious about what I'd been up to, where I'd been. But I was fairly sure I didn't warrant an airport alert. Besides, I'd come and gone so many times. And I spent lots of money. That's all that really mattered. They would let me go and expect me back. At the gate a uniformed security man studied my passport. He flicked through the pages, stopped and looked into my eyes, giving me a hard stare. I smiled. He stamped my visa and waved me to the ticket barrier.

A little crazy is good.
Yamilia Mena Lopez

MADRID

At Madrid airport I had a four-hour wait for my connecting flight to Heathrow. This was the old airport, just before the magnificent structure they have now. I remember that Paul hated it, refused to take any flights connecting there. My stomach was churning with butterflies and, despite not sleeping on the flight, I was wide awake. I knew rum was a bad idea, but that's exactly what I wanted, what my body needed. I settled for a mojito. Cut down slowly, be sensible. I was on my third and quite mellow when I took out my wallet to check how much English money I had.

I stared at the money Paul had sent me. I counted it on the bar, oblivious to the stares of the barman and fellow drinkers. Nearly five-hundred dollars. But $4200 was still available from ATMs. I looked around me, suddenly confused at my surroundings. This was Madrid. What was I doing here? Why had I boarded that flight? Because I thought I had to. Because I had been building up to it for days, preparing myself, steeling myself. But I had money. We could buy a car with that. I could give Tony some money to keep him happy. I would have a small income. I could start again, build up slowly, try not to make the same mistakes this time. Would they allow me back in?

My hands were shaking. And something more. Something pleasant and, at the same time, very uncomfortable. I wanted to lie down. Suddenly I wanted to sleep. I put my wallet away and tried to think, took slow sips of my mojito. Be calm body, please be calm, help me out here. How many times had I asked that? Asked my body to perform for just one more day, just get me through this and I'll look after you – stop smoking and drinking, exercise, eat well – I promise. I bought another drink and concentrated on my breathing, slow deep breaths through the nose, deep into my lungs, out slowly then hold, repeat. I had a coughing fit.

I called Paul's mobile. He was at Heathrow.

'So they let you out?' I said. 'What are you doing there?'

'Yes, thanks for that, a minor setback. I'm thinking about a trip somewhere, not fucking Cuba. I'm in the bar. Haven't made up my mind yet. Having a look at what other people are up to. Might follow some silly tarts somewhere nice. Where are you?'

'Madrid. The airport.'

'You have a habit of ending up in my least favourite places. What are you doing there? Why aren't you in Cuba? Did you get the money?'

'Thanks, yes. I think I may have ended up here by mistake. How much money did you make?'

'Enough to send five to you and have a little break for myself.'

At least twenty, I thought. Another five would be nice.

I really could set myself up with that. I asked for ten. We argued back and forth for a while.

'All right, I'll let you have another five. Where shall I send it?'

I thought about that. My flight to Heathrow was in an hour. Or I could just stay at the airport and get the next available flight back to Havana. I didn't know what to do.

'Can you send it here,' I said, 'to one of the banks here?'

That would give me a choice: London or Havana.

'I suppose so, but why? Why the fuck do you want to stay in that dump?'

'I may go back to Cuba.'

'Is that wise?'

'Probably not,' I said.

GLOSSARY

Barrio: neighbourhood.

Casa Particular: A private house rented as accommodation for tourists; sometimes available for amorous assignations, where a room or house is rented for a brief period.

CDR: *Committee for the Defence of the Revolution*: A network of neighbourhood committees across Cuba. They supposedly keep a file revealing the behaviour, moral and political, of every resident and by extension, every Cuban citizen and visitor. In two years I was only made aware of their presence twice, both in extreme and justified circumstances. My opinion, based on experience, is that their role is more social and community orientated: education, medical care, festivals and dealing with the aftermath of hurricanes.

Cristal: Popular bottled or canned beer.

Mojito: White rum, lime juice, sparkling water, sugar and mint; mellow but ultimately lethal.

Obispo: A long narrow street in Old Havana. The Ambos Mundos hotel where Hemingway wrote *For Whom the Bell*

Tolls is at one end and the El Floridita bar where he drank Daiquiris is at the other. Between the two runs Obispo, popular for shopping, bars and promenading. The events recounted here took place at a time when the bars still remained open all night; they now shut at midnight so as not to disturb tourists. Other bars can be found.

Paladares: Small family restaurants run under government licence. Privately owned restaurants were illegal under the revolution, but after the collapse of communism and the loss of Soviet investment, the Cuban government was forced to relax some economic restrictions. The Paladar is often a family's front room with two or three tables, home-cooked food to order and friendly service; they can be hard to find and are often discovered through recommendation. Until recently Paladares operated under restrictive rules, but Raul Castro (Fidel's younger brother) has eased or removed many restrictions as private enterprise is encouraged.

Peso Economy: The events recounted here took place when the dual economy consisted of US dollars and the Cuban peso. The dollar retained its exchange rate value and prices in dollars were similar to those in the UK: a pair of reasonable trainers might cost $80 or £50. Cuban pesos were worth perhaps a twentieth or 5% of the dollar and purchased only Cuban goods: subsidised food or utilities, for example. The average wage was $10 a month, most people working alternate days; a teacher, scientist or doctor might earn $40 a month. Cubans surviving within the system couldn't hope to achieve parity with the dollar or buy the goods in the dollar shops available to tourists and, increasingly, Cubans with dollars. So there were two economies, the dollar and the peso. Those in the tourist industry received tips and some could prosper; a skilled professional might supplement their income driving a taxi or waiting tables. Many Cubans receive money from relatives in the USA, particularly Miami. There is a growing middle-class, partly funded by US relatives, partly entrepreneurial. José supported himself and his family through living by his wits, hustling and befriending tourists. The dollar has since been replaced with the CUC, the Cuban Convertible Peso. It is worth the same as the dollar, but can only be obtained and used in Cuba. Cubans now receive a portion of their wages in CUCs, but the system remains much the same.

Santeria: A religion consisting of an enjoyable mixture of Catholicism and African belief brought with the slaves of the Spanish Empire. It is far too complicated to explain – see my experiences.

Silver Dry: Main drink of choice: 5 year old white rum, 37.5% proof.